Diana Sanders lives in Oxford with her husband, Mo Chandler, and two cats. She works as a psychologist and has published five previous books on health and psychology. She enjoys walking, travelling, spending time with friends and family, and just being alive.

www.dianasanders.net

Will I Still Be Me?

A journey through a transplant

Will I Still Be Me?
A journey through a transplant

Diana Sanders

DAY BOOKS
OXFORDSHIRE

ISBN 10: 0953 2213 8 5

ISBN 13: 978 0953 2213 8 7

British Library Cataloguing in Publication Data

A catalogue record for this book is available from the British Library

This edition first published by Day Books, July 2006

© Diana Sanders, 2006

The moral rights of the author have been asserted

Printed in the UK by the Alden Press, Oxford. This publication is printed on acid-free paper

Day Books, Orchard Piece, Crawborough, Charlbury, Oxfordshire OX7 3TX, UK
www.day-books.com

Contents

The End of the Beginning

2nd November 2002

THIS MORNING I DECIDE to go into town. Had I decided last night, I would have spent dark hours doing battle with what-ifs crawling around my head: what if I am ill? What if I feel strange? What if I am sick all over the place? In spite of having made up my mind, I search for excuses. Mo has a dentist's appointment.

'Won't you want me to be here when you get back?' I ask him. 'They may need to take the tooth out.'

'No.'

'But I should be here, you've done so much for me ...'

'No,' he insists.

'Maybe it's too early?'

'No. Just go.'

He is holding my jacket out for me. 'Just go.'

At the bus-stop, a small crowd has gathered. This is the first time I have been out alone for nearly two years. I want to tell everyone 'Look at me!' like a small child bouncing on a space-hopper. I start chatting to a smiley girl, and soon the conversation – grumblings about Oxford's bus service, the weather, the broken pane in the shelter – ripples through the other people. A neighbour, for years disgruntled with me because of a long-forgotten disagreement, greets me warmly: 'I am so pleased to see you. You look so well.' I love her. I love them all. The bus finally arrives thirty minutes late. The driver rebuffs criticism: 'I'm not late, I'm early – I had to leave early, the ten-past and twenty-past haven't even arrived yet.' I find this hilarious, and picture myself grabbing him and planting huge lipstick kisses on his cheeks. I go upstairs on the bus. Upstairs! I've not been able to climb up the stairs for years. The front seat is empty – I am truly blessed.

In town I am jostled and buffeted by people, people everywhere. Happy, bored, indifferent, wrinkled, smiling, scowling people. The *Big Issue* seller, standing on the corner. '*Big Issue. Big Issue,*' he calls, hopefully. The alcoholic people in Bonn Square, lethargic souls, long abandoned. Homeless people lying in corners. The rules and regulations of childhood come back: 'Always share.' 'Think of the poor starving Biafrans.' 'One good turn deserves another.' The balance-sheet of life. How can I ever balance the gift I have been given? I want to take these people home and look after them. Walk into the building society, empty my account and hand cash around like sweeties.

I go up to the *Big Issue* seller and buy three. Give him ten pounds – 'Keep the change.' I walk on and see another, outside Marks and Spencer's. I buy four. Ten pounds.

'Keep the change,' I say to him.

'Thanks, love. You have a good heart,' he replies.

I laugh and agree. 'A very good heart. It's second-hand. I'm a great believer in recycling.'

He looks puzzled and I chortle to myself. Clutching seven copies of the *Big Issue*, I am starting to flag. I cannot think why I came into town in the first place. I stand at the corner, puzzled, distracted, worried that I am going to start feeling sick. A woman with tight white curls peeping from a floral headscarf, thick tweed coat buttoned up to the neck, comes up to me, takes one of my *Big Issues*, and presses a pound coin into my hand.

'Good luck, dear,' she wishes me.

As if I need any more good luck.

1. Sulking
1956–1979

WHEN I WAS A CHILD, my ambition was to be a grown-up. Not that I saw anything particularly wonderful about being grown-up. I liked being a child, the youngest of three girls until my brother came along when I was ten. I could never work out how old grown-ups were. When I asked my mother her age she would only tell me 'I am as old as my tongue and a little older than my teeth,' which puzzled me for a long time until I saw my new baby brother's gummy, toothless mouth and watched as his teeth appeared, one by one. Grown-ups led their lives by rules written in invisible ink only to appear when transgressed. As children our job was either to stick to the rules, if we could see any benefits in doing so, or break them without being found out.

'Don't talk with your mouth full.' 'Don't play with your food.' 'Don't get drawn into a hysterical story with your sisters, winding yourselves up to fever pitch – it will end in tears.' And a set of rules reserved specifically for me: 'Don't run.' 'Don't get too tired.' 'You have to go to hospital every few months.' 'Don't wear yourself out.' I learned, early on, that becoming a grown-up might not be for me.

I was born with a congenital heart condition and grew into a rather skinny, sickly child with the determination of a rottweiler. During development, something had gone wrong with my heart.

I learned at the age of five that all was not well. It had been apparent to my mother much earlier, landed with a scrawny baby who was sick after every feed. She fed and mopped, mopped and fed and tried to find a doctor who would take her concerns seriously. Her GP reassured her that all was well, believing her to be an over-anxious mother. I carried on vomiting and refusing to grow and her GP carried on telling her not to worry. Finally I was referred to Dr Victoria Smallpeice, a warm and efficient woman who took one look at me and diagnosed renal failure. At the age of one, I had an operation to remove my diseased left kidney. It then also became clear that there was something wrong with my heart.

When I reached five, I was old enough to be investigated further. The test, a cardiac catheterisation, involved inserting a tiny tube into my heart through a vein in my arm, in order to measure the pressures in the heart. Adults can remain awake during the procedure, but a boisterous five-year-old needed a general anaesthetic. I remember my excitement at hearing I was to go into hospital. It seemed such an exotic and grown-up thing to do, to spend time in a different place by myself. I packed all my favourite things into a bag – my small knitted bear called FiFi, a toy cat given to me in 1959 when we came home on the *Queen Mary* after a year in America, my teddy bear and a doll 'borrowed' from my sisters. I was given a new colouring set, a new nightie and new books and it was not even my birthday. The night before, I was too excited to sleep. In 1961 it was thought that children settle better in hospital if the parents left them there: and however much a mother wanted to stay, it was simply not allowed. So, after being taken to a small ward, changed into my new nightie and put to bed, my mother left me. It was probably only for a short time. But through the eyes of a five-year-old, it was an enormous shock.

I stood up in the cot and screamed. Where was Mummy? Why was I in a cot, not a big girl's bed? I had been abandoned for ever. The nurse came to offer comfort, or tell me to shut up, I don't remember, but I was inconsolable. The time has always stuck in my mind, leaving vivid memories and a dread of being left alone in a strange place. I have been alone many times, have travelled to New Zealand alone, hitchhiked alone, lived alone and enjoyed my own company. But I still do not like being alone in hospitals.

The episode only made real sense to me later on when, as a psychologist, I came across the work of John Bowlby, and James and Joyce Robertson. The photographs in their book *Separation and the Very Young*, showing children in hospitals, separated from their mothers, could have been of me. The children looked enraged, protesting, and – if left long enough – despondent in their despair. Bowlby's work was eventually to have a profound impact on the way children are treated. These days, children are not left alone in hospital; a parent can stay in the same room, even go into the anaesthetic room and be there when the child recovers from surgery. The first I knew about having had an operation was when I woke up in my cot with a bandage on my arm, my mother not to be seen anywhere. I felt like screaming: and scream I did.

When I came back from hospital, my mother explained the results of the test. I was in bed and she sat next to me, holding my hand, talking in her Very Serious Voice. She told me I had a hole in my heart. My eyes wide, I tried to understand. For once, I was stuck for words and nodded mutely. She tucked me up and put out the light. I heard her going down the stairs and shutting the living room door. Murmurs of talking, the radio. In the quiet, I felt my heart beating. A hole must mean that it is leaking – like the hot-water bottle that split in my bed the previous week, bursting rubber-smelly water all over the sheets. So, I might leak blood. I checked where it might come from. I must be like a hot-water bottle, blood sloshing all over the place just beneath the skin. No wonder everyone made such a fuss when I cut myself. In the dark, I tried to slow my heart down – if it wasn't beating so hard, then maybe I would leak less. That night I took a long time to get to sleep. I worked out that this fact must be worth something. When I went back to school, proud of my new knowledge, I announced at break that I had a hole in my heart. My friends were unimpressed. 'Don't be so stupid – you'd be dead,' they said and turned their attention back to their games. I knew something was different about me, but what? I decided to talk to my older sister. From her nine-year-old height, she looked down her nose at me and said, wisely, 'It means you've only got half a heart.'

One consequence of my half heart was having to go for regular investigations. I became an expert on surviving hospital waiting rooms. I liked Dr Smallpeice, who always had a kind word and a sweet or two. The Churchill Hospital in Oxford, then and until recently a series of Nissen huts in the middle of a field, was well-resourced for children – murals in the waiting room, toys to play with, windows to look out of, books to read. Dr Smallpeice was always pleased with my progress and I came out feeling proud of myself. Interminable waiting, but entertainment on tap. My cardiology appointments in the Radcliffe Infirmary were something else. A huge impersonal waiting area, uncomfortable seats, endless waits, nothing much to do except read whatever I had brought along, which lasted about five minutes. Then trying to pass the time in a state of boredom, fidgeting, looking for crumbs of distraction. When we finally got to see the consultant, things went from bad to worse. I took one look at him and decided to hate him.

Dr Lee was tall, willowy and superior, with sharp features that reminded me of a crow. Having made the decision to hate him, I had to stick to it at all costs. I've since met Dr Lee in later life and realise that I was wrong. He is a striking-looking man who was very committed to helping me and the family. I've read my medical notes from childhood, full of detailed letters between him and other hospitals in London and America looking for the best form of treatment. He was supportive to my parents and in short bent over backwards to help. But to me, as a child, he was the enemy. I decided that whatever advice he gave me I would do the opposite.

During our consultations, he would ask me to go into the examination room and shut the door while he talked to my mother. This was a total affront to me. An enraged six-year-old, then seven-, eight-, nine-year-old, I would open the door a crack and listen to what they were saying, later to tell my mother off for any inaccuracies.

I realise now that he was looking after her, reassuring her, helping with the terrible anxiety and responsibility that my parents must have carried throughout my childhood and beyond. But from the self-centred, selfish view of a child, such treatment was an affront to my very soul. It was my body and how dare anyone shut me out. I stood, arms crossed, lower lip pouting, huffing and puffing silently with the sheer indignity and unfairness of it all. Understandable, perhaps, in a six-year-old, less so when I still, occasionally, some forty years later, respond to any medical indignities with a stiff reprimand. During a routine check-up in my thirties, when I was looking fit and well, the registrar looked at my notes, then at me and said 'To look at you, no one would know you're such a cripple,' to which I responded 'To listen to you, no one would know you're an intelligent human being.'

My regular check-ups very often led to nothing more than further check-ups, but occasionally would result in a host of investigations. When I was fourteen, my ever-accompanying mother and I went up to London for further tests. I had the honour of lying on a bed surrounded by a crowd of young medical students, all men, listening to my chest through a communal stethoscope. I wasn't the most streetwise or self-assured young thing. I remained stubbornly flat-chested until I was fifteen, much to the chagrin of my sisters who would only take me with them to the Saturday-night discos if I wore a bra stuffed with socks. Braced, knock-kneed and spotty, I was hardly likely to attract admiring looks. Something, however, must have been awakening in me, shy glances, some assessment of who might be the most handsome, collecting information to giggle over later with my sisters. This round of tests led inevitably to another catheterisation, but this time I had wised-up. 'What is it worth?' I said to my mother. Assured that I would get a new herringbone coat out of the deal, I went ahead, quite enjoying the time out of school.

All these tests were to see if surgery was a possibility. It wasn't. Too risky. It would kill me.

Today, babies with my congenital heart condition are operated on soon after birth, thanks to the pioneering work of Professor Sir Magdi Yacoub. In the 1950s and 1960s the technology was not available, so I had to live with it. I had no choice in the matter. I had to put up with my heart.

What were the consequences for me and my life? Nothing and everything. Nothing in the sense of having a pretty normal upbringing and entering the rough-and-tumble of life with as much gusto as any other child. I do not remember being molly-coddled, or feeling special or important. My parents and school had the wisdom not to make a big fuss about it all. I had to work as hard as any other child, was told off as much and not sheltered from the inevitable rows and difficulties of childhood because I was too 'frail'. Despite this semblance of normality, I was also supposed to live by the rules: be careful, don't run around, take life easy. Fuelled by my hatred of all things medical and my stubborn, six-year-old self deciding that whatever I was told I would have a go at the opposite, I lived my life to prove them all wrong. In fact, the rules were often vague and open to interpretation and I worked out early on that I needed to sort them for myself. I had a go at games and sports and probably could have continued if I had been any good. Sadly, my response to a tennis-ball coming in my direction was to shut my eyes and duck, and I completely lacked any competitive edge in games. If someone else really wanted to win, well, let them, I didn't mind. Which made me a pretty bad sport and no one wanted to play with me anyway.

How much of this was compensation for not being able to do it physically, I do not know. Exercise was, in all honesty, hard work – a short burst of exertion, running around, cycling too fast, even shrieking with laughter, would leave me gasping for breath, my mouth and fingers turning blue, which I could use as a party-trick to entertain my friends. I was always lagging behind. On walks up to the park, my friends had to hang around 'waiting for Di,' or 'waiting to die' as they called it. I was skinny and scrawny and lived up to my nicknames 'Spindle' and, with reference to the fact that my legs were so thin, it was lucky that they did not break, 'Lucky Legs'. I got tired, frustrated at not being able to keep up. But nothing disastrous seemed to happen if I did overdo things. I would have to stop and catch my breath, pick myself up off the floor on occasions and I would sometimes get ill, such as the time when my friends and I decided to go for a 15-mile bicycle ride which put me in bed for a week. But I always seemed to pick up, so all these restrictions on my life could not be completely necessary.

Academic work was something else. At the age of fourteen or so, I discovered that I enjoyed working and learning and, if I tried, could do well in tests and exams, so that was where my energy went. Academic work was something I could be good at, when all else was a non-starter. I could get off games if I complained about being too tired and sit in the dining-room doing my homework while my friends slogged it out on the hockey-pitch, returning cold and wet and muddy with bruised shins from deliberate attacks from the latest school bully.

I finished school and went to Durham University to study psychology. In fact, ironically, I originally applied to study medicine. Despite my hatred of most medics, I was fascinated by the subject even from early days. My mother was a medical researcher, my father a physicist, and one sister had trained as a doctor, so I inherited a fascination with human biology. I wanted to speak the language of the medics so they could not talk down to me. After leaving school in the summer of 1974, having decided on a gap year to be followed by a career in medicine, I came across books on Freud and Jung and decided that, rather than understand the workings of the body, the mind was where the action was. I got a bus up to Durham from Oxford and sat outside the professor's office in the psychology department and waited until he had five minutes to see me. A serious, skinny and over-earnest eighteen-year-old, I explained to him that I had decided I wanted to study psychology at Durham and he needed to make a place available for me to start in a month's time. I gave the head of one of the nearby colleges the same treatment. Quite what their motivation was in moving heaven and earth to get me not only a place in the university but also in a college, I am not sure; possibly they were sorry for me or amused by my presumptuousness. The strategy seemed to work and I started at Durham that year and went on to get a first. I studied hard at university, but I also used it as a testing-ground for my physical limits – having been restricted at home, I tried out whatever would make Dr Lee or my mother draw a sharp intake of breath. I joined the speleological society and, dangling on a rope at the top of an underground waterfall, soaked and exhausted, discovered my height phobia. To my secret relief, the cave-rescue team banned me from any further expeditions. I played squash, not well and usually by myself, bashing the ball against the walls of an empty court, but at least I gave it a go; and I walked. And walked and walked.

Walking was my passion and my enemy. I discovered I could walk for miles so long as it was flat or downhill and so long as it was not too cold. Or windy. And I had had enough sleep the night before. I walked in Northumberland and, when I moved to Edinburgh after my first degree, I headed for the Pentlands, Arran Island, Torriden, Mull. As soon as a hill approached, I had to slow down or stop. As a child, my sister Annie would stick me on her back and carry me up the hill, a practice she continued well into our thirties. Away from home it was hardly fair to ask my walking companions to carry me, so I learned the fine art of struggling without being too obvious. I was renowned for my regular stops for food and drink, or to study the view, for my sudden interest in the grass beneath my feet or a common flower. I must have been as irritating as hell on those hills, requiring the whole walking-party to stop with me in case I got lost, but I carried on walking and people seemed to tolerate me with good humour. Now, I have no patience at all for people walking slowly, but then I was just grateful for my friends who let me get away with it.

I learned early on that I needed to make up my own rules. One was to give everything a go if I wanted to. Just stop and get my breath when I need to, then carry on. Don't make a song and dance about it. I never liked explaining to people what was wrong – it was complicated and unless they were medical, hard to understand. If I did explain, sometimes people would be apologetic and say 'I'm sorry,' which just irritated me, or they would sympathetic which I could not bear. From early on, I never wanted people to feel sorry for me. Sorry was for people in wheelchairs, children born without limbs, people who didn't make an effort to overcome their problems, not me. And I didn't want people to make a fuss, to molly-coddle me, or, crucially, to try and stop me doing things. My stock response was to say 'It's fine, not a problem, just something I live with,' and rapidly change the subject. My rule was to act normal at all times and not say anything unless necessary.

So, restrictions could be got over and, with a bit of adaptation, a bit of time stopping for breath, I could lead my life completely normally. Every restriction but one. For all but one, I was determined not to take too much notice and get on with my life. I huffed and puffed my way through childhood, through adolescence and through university, regularly going blue as I tested yet another limit. But what really brought me up short was when I was told that I could not have children.

2. My Half a Heart

1979–1994

AT LEAST EIGHT IN EVERY thousand children are born with a heart defect. Many of these are minor and cause no problems, such as mitral valve prolapse or other leaky valves. A lot of people go through life with unusual heart structures without even being aware of them. About half of those born with heart conditions will need medical treatment or surgery. So-called 'blue babies' have a range of disorders such as a gap between the right and left atria or ventricles, a so called 'hole in the heart', or abnormal or missing heart valves, arteries or veins.

People born with congenital heart conditions face physical limitations and an uncertain life span. Many get tired and breathless and undergo numerous medical investigations and operations. A proportion die at a young age. And many women with heart problems face difficulties with pregnancy or birth. In very rare cases, the cardiac abnormalities are genetic and can be passed on to the children – then, serious decisions have to be made. For others, the changes in the circulation during pregnancy are too much for an already overloaded cardiovascular system to cope with. Pregnancy may cause blood clots to develop, increasing the risk of a stroke. Some people have abnormal heart rhythms which can be fatal. Most importantly, many people with congenital heart conditions face challenges with simply getting through day to day – getting up, going to work, shopping, cooking, walking, whatever, all conducted within a cloud of low energy or

20

exhaustion. How can we possibly breathe for other people when we have enough trouble breathing for ourselves?

Of all this I was blissfully ignorant until my early twenties. I had not thought about children. My mother produced, I believed at the time in response to my request, a fourth child at the age of forty. So, at ten, I had a baby brother and had direct experience of all that a new baby brings – the joy and delight but also the nappies, sleepless nights, dribble and snot, unpredictability, difficulties in lifting him as he became bigger, strength required to push a pram, constant observation and responsibility. I loved him to bits, loved feeding him and cuddling him and, along with my sisters, loved dressing him up in girls' clothes and generally tormenting him. But as far as I was concerned I'd had my fun with babies and wouldn't consider having any for myself. Faced with the knowledge that I did not have a choice, that was a different matter.

Dr Lee and I did battle during my childhood and adolescence in Oxford, but my yearly check-ups stopped when I left home for university and I decided I did not want any further contact with cardiologists. But I was advised to seek another cardiac opinion when I was doing my PhD in Edinburgh. I'd been to the family planning clinic there to find out if it was all right to take the pill. The new consultant I was referred to had clearly never been to a 'Breaking Bad News' seminar. He took one look at me, and came out with: 'You *do* know that you cannot have children.' No preamble, no discussion, no follow-up, nothing. He offered to perform another catheterisation just to check that he was right. Somehow the logic behind his chosen order of events eluded me – it seemed too big a pronouncement to make unless he was entirely sure. I duly went through my third catheterisation, much more fun than the others since I told all my friends to come and visit and come and visit they did, in gangs clustered around the bed, eating grapes. No compensation at all for the hour after the catheterisation, when the doctor reiterated his first message: 'The pressures are just too high – you'd never survive a pregnancy. You should get yourself sterilised.'

So what exactly was causing all the problems? In order to understand, I had to get to grips with cardiology, shrouded in mystery and long words, all to describe what is, in essence, a central-heating system.

A normal heart is made up of two pumps designed to propel blood through two different circuits – the first between the body and the heart, the second, between the heart and the lungs. Blood going from the body to the heart, then to the lungs is deoxygenated, or blue – the cold circuit. Blood travelling from the lungs to the heart and then on to the body is oxygenated, red blood – the hot circuit. The heart itself consists of four chambers – a right and left atrium at the top and a right and left ventricle below. The right atrium collects deoxygenated 'blue' blood from the body, pumps it into the right ventricle, then on to the lungs via the pulmonary artery. There, the blue blood picks up oxygen and returns to the left side of the heart. Here it is pumped from the left atrium to the left ventricle. The left ventricle's job is to get blood from the heart throughout the body via the aorta and so it is the largest pumping chamber, operating at high pressure – the circulation between the heart and lungs, in contrast, is at low pressure. For all the time that we are alive, be-it one minute or one hundred years, the heart is pumping blood to and fro, to and fro. A fantastically sophisticated but simple organ, so sophisticated that there are lots of opportunities for things to go wrong.

And go wrong they do. During embryonic development, the heart starts as a tube, analogous to the simple heart tube found in worms, then changes to become a four chambered pump. The heart's complicated evolution during the time that we are embryos presents the opportunity for many different types of congenital defects to occur. A tiny minority are genetic, either a single mutant gene or chromosomal abnormality such as Down syndrome – around half of these children have cardiac abnormalities. A very small number of cases of congenital heart conditions are caused by environmental factors, one being exposure to the rubella virus during the first three months of pregnancy. Other viruses, or medication, may be responsible. In the majority of cases the cause of the defect is simply not known.

In my case the pulmonary artery and aorta swapped places: the aorta, rather than coming out of the high-pressure left ventricle, arises from the low-pressure right ventricle and the pulmonary artery arises from the high-pressure left ventricle. This swap is known as transposition of the great vessels. It means trouble – two closed circuits, deoxygenated blue blood coming from the right atria, into the right ventricle and then off back to the body via the aorta, pumping blue blood to and from the body, bypassing the lungs completely. The pulmonary circulation, in contrast, is doing its own thing, pumping the oxygenated red blood merrily to and from the lungs. Result, a non-sustainable system and death. In my case, however, something rather clever happened to cope with this non-starter system – a hole developed between the left and right ventricles, so at least some of the oxygenated blood from the lungs could get back to the body. For other babies with simple transpositions, no such hole develops, and in order for the baby to stay alive following birth, a hole is created surgically between the ventricles.

The medical description of my heart condition is 'anatomically corrected transposition of the great vessels with a ventricular septal defect and pulmonary hypertension', or Eisenmenger syndrome. Victor Eisenmenger was an Austrian physician and near-contemporary of Sigmund Freud, another Austrian who was to have a big influence on my life. Eisenmenger described a thirty-two-year-old man with exercise intolerance, cyanosis (blueness on exercise), haemoptysis (spitting blood) and heart-failure. On post-mortem examination, the unfortunate young man was found to have a large ventricular septal defect with pulmonary hypertension. This identical condition was first discovered in me when I was five and still very much alive. Deoxygenated blood circulated around my body, resulting in tiredness, fatigue and breathlessness. As soon as the heart speeds up to respond to exercise, more deoxygenated blood is pumped creating more breathlessness. Throughout my life, taking a run at anything was impossible – rather than a burst of oxygen hitting my system, the already low levels would decline even further, so stairs, hills, running,

23

jumping, dancing, cycling and other energetic pastimes would have me in a heap on the floor, gasping for breath. The converse was true, luckily for me. Anything conducted as a metaphorical heap on the floor – sex, studying, thinking, talking, reading, even swimming, was fine. The other effect was that blood passed from the heart to the lungs at very high pressure – the pressure needed to pump blood to the body from the large left ventricle was instead delivering blood to the more fragile lungs, causing pulmonary hypertension and gradual lung damage.

It had all worked fine for me so far. I had to be reasonably sensible, I got tired and breathless, but I could do most things. I would not make a marathon runner or Olympic swimmer, but I could walk, cycle and swim slowly, and work as hard as anyone else. But clearly, all was not to be normal in the reproductive department. Strangely, I had actually been sexually active for a few years before anyone saw fit to tell me to take extra precautions.

But sterilised? What a word. How clean, astringent, medical. How empty, sad, barren. My training in not-taking-much-notice-of-what-the-doctors-say meant that I questioned it. I asked for another opinion from another doctor in the Edinburgh hospital, as well as Dr Lee, rather to my chagrin, but to whom my feelings were beginning to defrost with the onset of slight maturity. Luckily for me, too, I had a good relationship with my doctor at the family-planning clinic, deeply sympathetic, distressed when I told her the news, who insisted that I see the clinic social worker for counselling before I make any final decisions. 'In the meantime, be careful, won't you?' she advised. Advice I did take, although part of me, the small stubborn child with the pouting lip, wanted to go out and shag for Scotland and get pregnant just to prove them wrong. I realised the stakes were a bit high for that. I sat in the library, poring through medical texts. My chances of surviving a pregnancy were less than 50 per cent, I learned. In other words, more than a one in two chance of dying during pregnancy. Multiple complications can set in after delivery, risking bleeding to death. Fetal mortality was more than 25 per cent and even if a baby did survive, as my social worker pointed out, what would it be like for that baby if I didn't make it? Big, big questions and big, big probabilities not pointing favourably in my direction. The cruel irony of it all was that I was studying for a PhD on psychological changes during the menstrual cycle, working at the Reproductive Biology Unit of the Department of Obstetrics and Gynaecology in Edinburgh University, a unit focused on all things to do with promoting and preventing procreation – ways to have them if you couldn't and ways to stop them if you could. And I was getting to the age where friends were starting their own reproduction.

After a year of talking, thinking, crying, puzzling, I decided to get myself sterilised. Just before Christmas, at the age of twenty-three, I was admitted for a tubal ligation to the very hospital I worked in, to a ward full of women having terminations. This time, no friends, no gang, no party, just me. My housemate picked me up from the hospital, sore and shocked and sat me in front of a coal fire with tea and tissues. I went home to Oxford for a rather bleak Christmas, unable to talk much about what had happened. I numbed out, shut down, pretended it didn't matter. After all, I was an academic – I was writing a PhD thesis, writing papers, giving talks, becoming a researcher. Not surprisingly, my menstrual cycle shut down as well, everything shut down: I was celibate for two years, keeping myself to myself, trying not to care too much.

It was a remark from a would-be suitor in Bristol, when I returned from a year working in New Zealand, that opened up the floodgates: 'But that must hurt like hell – deep down, every woman wants children. You must feel awful.' I did. I started crying then and continued, on and off, until I was thirty-five. I was not incapacitated – I was enjoying life, working hard, doing research, getting married and divorced and re-married, partying, travelling – a life worth living. But I had to go through the grief of the loss. My friends had children and I smiled and joined in their joy, while weeping quietly inside. I had to find answers to the inevitable questions, 'Do you have children?' or even, 'How old are your children?' When I said no, no children, I would try and change the subject before the next question: 'Any plans?' Sometimes I would explain and would then get drawn into a conversation about the disadvantages of having children, as though hearing about parent's moans was supposed to make me feel better. I couldn't feel better. When my eldest sister, Chris, gave birth to her first child in 1986, the family congregated at my parents' house to celebrate. I smiled and laughed and congratulated, then, when everyone was getting noisily sozzled after dinner, I crept up to the spare room where baby Jamie was asleep. I sat and watched him in the dark and picked him up and held him, weeping wet tears on his downy head. As he slept his baby-deep sleep, I vowed that I would try, at least, to be a good auntie to him.

A big part of it, for me, was not having any choice. I do not know whether or when I may have chosen to have children if it had been possible – maybe a case of the grass being greener. I was angry, too, about the way it had been presented as a decision made for me by the medics. There were so many ways that it could have been introduced to me, with more gentle explanations of the risks. Perhaps I could have been given the option to take the risk, knowing that the NHS would support me – I now know of women who have children, successfully, against medical advice. Maybe I could have acted differently. Who knows? I do know that having got through to thirty-five, watching my sisters and friends produce babies left right and centre, any desire, any maternal urge, simply switched off. The grief felt as though it had passed as a huge storm, followed by peace. I did not mind any more. My new husband, Mo and I seriously considered the possibility of adoption, but rejected it after a short time – our lives were too full of other things to want to change and introduce the element of children. We had children, anyway – by now three nephews and a niece on my side, and five on his, and access to friends' children anytime we wanted to play. And by this time, it was becoming enough problem running my own life, let alone being responsible for any small dependents. In fact, I was myself becoming a bit of a liability.

3. Running on Empty

1995–2000

I AM NOT SURE WHERE I got the idea that I would not survive very long, but it is something I have always carried around with me. No matter how much my parents concealed their anxiety, some of it must have rubbed off quite young. I never felt particularly anxious about my health, seeing it as something to be challenged, beaten, sorted out, managed. A problem to live round. I was never told of the dire consequences of overdoing things. I think there were real concerns about my heart not being able to stand up to chronic overload, but the failsafe system of instant breathlessness when I over-exerted myself meant it was almost impossible to keep going – gasping for breath, I simply had to stop. But what I picked up was that life, for me, was unlikely to be long. My work gave me unlimited access to medical libraries. I read and gleaned that, in general, people with Eisenmenger syndrome did not usually survive beyond the second or third decade. I'd made it to my third decade already so was doing well, but probably needed to hedge my bets. If life was to be short, I would simply do what any normal person would do, only faster.

As Samuel Johnson said, nothing concentrates the mind so much as the prospect of being hanged: and so life became focused. If I wanted to get on with something, or go somewhere, I needed to do so as soon as possible. I was constantly fitting everything in. The candle was to be burned not only at both ends but in the middle as well. Keep busy, keep going, whatever. In my twenties and thirties, this seemed to work. At least, I got away with it in most areas of life. By the time I was thirty-five I'd lived in Oxford, Australia, Durham, Edinburgh, New Zealand, Bristol and Devon, but I settled back in Oxford in 1984. I got married, unwisely, when I was twenty-nine, mainly because I had not been married before and thought it was about time I gave it a go. Not surprisingly my first marriage only lasted a short time and then I met Mo, who was to become my second husband, just before my divorce.

I worked hard to keep as well as possible, walking, swimming, doing yoga, finding ways to keep fit which did not involve pounding pavements or getting out of breath. Being a psychologist meant lots of opportunities to work in different areas and many of my jobs had a medical theme, reflecting perhaps what felt most familiar to me. After a series of research jobs, I trained in counselling and psychotherapy and worked in the psychology services in Oxford as a cognitive therapist, trying to help people cope with the problems life throws at them – stress, depression, anxiety, trauma, disability. I loved my work and, in the absence of children, it became pretty central to my life. Maybe my caring went into my patients; certainly, much of my energy went into my work. My hard work at school, throwing myself into academia being unable to succeed in the physical aspects of life, paid off. I had, if not a brilliant career, an interesting and enjoyable one. I did as well as I could, all things considered. What I wanted to do never quite matched what I was physically able to do, but much of the time this did not stop me having a go. I pushed on and would always go the extra mile for my work, occasionally to the detriment of myself. As I became a little more tired, a little more breathless in my thirties, I reduced my work to part-time to give myself, literally, a bit of breathing space.

I first started experiencing serious problems when I was thirty-nine. I returned from a holiday in South Africa in October 1995, full of a chest infection caught, no doubt, when cooped up in a cramped aeroplane for twelve hours. One night, a week after getting home, I turned over in bed to put out the light, and my heart took off – my pulse rate increased to 200 beats a minute and I could hardly breathe. I got out of bed and promptly fell on the floor. Convinced I must be having a panic attack, despite never having had one in my life and always ready to attribute anything to psychological causes, I sat on the floor and tried to calm myself down, breathing into a paper bag. 'Just calm down, relax,' I told myself. I didn't want to make a fuss, to waste anyone's time, so it was with extreme reluctance that I asked Mo to call the GP at midnight. A tired, harassed-looking deputy GP came round and looked puzzled, especially when she was unable to measure my blood pressure. She telephoned the hospital, who thought I better go in to have an ECG to check out what was happening. The GP then left us to our own devices.

Somehow, I got dressed and crawled down the stairs into the car, flopping forward in the seat like a mannequin. I felt sick, pains starting in my chest. My usual experiences of casualty was of having to wait for ages – instead, as soon as I got to the hospital, I was wheeled into a cubicle. Doctors gathered round my bed, attaching wires, putting lines in, looking worried. An intravenous drug to slow my heart rate failed to work. I needed a general anaesthetic and cardioversion, an electric shock to stop my heart and then re-start it. I did not like the sound of this and refused to have the anaesthetic, convinced that it would kill me: a six-year-old strop. Somehow I put up a fight until one of the doctors, a young South African, agreed to use a dose of tranquillisers instead. I came round from the procedure surrounded by bleeping machines and drips, my heart still racing, in the coronary care unit. Mo was sitting by the bed holding my hand.

This was to be the end of the honeymoon period when life could be lived comfortably alongside my heart condition. It was the end of me knowing what I feel when not affected by chemicals and the start of taking medication for the rest of my life. I was lucky to survive the episode, having had a severe supraventricular tachycardia which proved difficult to treat. Such arrhythmias are common in people with congenital heart conditions, I learned. Normally, the heart beats at a constant 60 to 80 beats per minute, increasing on exercise, stress or excitement. The rhythm of the heart is controlled by the pacemaker, the sino-atrial node, a group of cells in the right side of the heart where the electrical impulses start. The pacemaker kicks off an impulse which causes the atria to contract, followed by the ventricles, in a constant sequence. If one or more contractions get out of sequence, there are problems. In atrial fibrillation, electrical impulses start to arise from all over the atria, causing them to quiver rather than beat properly, causing a fast, uncontrolled heart rhythm. Because the heart chambers are not emptying properly, blood can pool and form clots, which can break off and travel to other parts of the body or brain, causing a stroke. I felt at the time as though my heart had gone mad, racing and leaping about, causing pain, faintness and breathlessness. That night I was lucky not to have a stroke, or worse. I later learned that I have inherited two clotting factors, protein C deficiency and prothrombin mutation, which increase the risk of clotting and so of stroke. Of this I was ignorant and regarded the whole episode as a major inconvenience. I was very cross at such a disruption to life and cross at being kept in the coronary care unit for six days. The impact on my life was huge, the turning-point when I could no longer ignore my heart or take my health for granted.

As always, I eventually picked up the pieces and got on with it, but was in a different place from where I had been before. I took several months to get used to taking the medication, which made me very sick at first, and took several months to forgive my heart for causing problems. Regular visits to the hospital became the norm. I became familiar with the procedure when my heart went out of rhythm, often at inconvenient times and in awkward places – in the swimming-pool; while shopping; while getting ready to go to work. Each time, I had to call for an ambulance, be carted into casualty and given whatever form of treatment was required. If I was lucky a short ride in an ambulance seemed to do the trick, in the way that a car trip to the vet would usually successfully cure whatever ailment our cats had been complaining of. If the ambulance did not do the trick – friends putting this down to my predilection for men in green uniforms – I was threatened with cardioversion. I did not know when my arrhythmias would happen, but decided I had to get on with life and just manage them when they did. A bloody-minded, six-year-old, stubborn way of coping, but it seemed to work. I settled for a slightly slower pace of life, reduced work a little and got on.

May 2000. I was alone in the house, trying to slow down and relax after a tiring day at work. My heart suddenly started imitating a spin-dryer with an uneven load. My pulse raced to over 200, I felt faint, managing to get to the phone before collapsing. I telephoned my neighbour, Anthony, who rushed round in more of a panic that I felt. Mayhem erupted. I lay on the floor trying to breathe, severe pains snaking up my chest, as Anthony called the ambulance, ran out to flag them down when they arrived, locking himself out of the house in the process. Somehow they all got back in and I was carted into the ambulance, which could not depart for the hospital since, somehow, the paramedic had then locked his resuscitation equipment in our house. All this excitement caused my heart to trip back into normal rhythm, in the way of kicking a wayward television. However, having got into the clutches of the medical system I stayed overnight in casualty, a regular. In the morning my consultant, Dr Gribbin, came to see me, beaming. Brian Gribbin had taken over when Dr Lee retired, and I had been seeing him since 1984 when I began to resume regular contact with the medical services. I liked Dr Gribbin enormously. He spoke my language, was willing to do business with me in a straightforward, honest way. He was blunt, called a spade a spade. He treated me as an equal and I listened to him.

'You again,' he said, sitting on the bed, explaining my heart condition to the accompanying medical student. Sometimes the consultant would ask the medical students to have a listen to my heart and try and make a diagnosis. I felt sorry for them and would whisper a few hints: 'Think pulmonary hypertension. Think transposition. Look at my toes.'

'What are we going to do with you?' Dr Gribbin put his hand on my arm, a warm gesture.

'What are you going to do with me? I'm sure my vet could put me out of my misery,' I replied.

He smiled. 'How about we ask the transplant unit at Papworth to review you?'

'I'm really not that bad yet, am I? Apart from the atrial fibrillation, I mean – I'm still working, swimming …' I tried to defend myself, desperate to be let out, to carry on as normal.

'Yes, but for how much longer?' The Scottish bluntness.

'OK then, I'll go to Papworth, that's fine.'

'Let's see what they have to say. Meanwhile, increase the Amiodarone. And keep taking it.' He patted my hand. From him I knew this was support and encouragement, not patronising.

'I do. I'm very good, really. I always do what the doctor says.'

He looked disbelieving. 'I'll see you in three months.' They moved away from my bed and I overheard Dr Gribbin describing me to the student as 'an independent thinker'.

The possibility of a transplant had been on the cards for a long time. I generally dismissed it, Scarlett O'Hara style, as something to be thought about 'tomorrow.' In my twenties, while working in Edinburgh, I remember a telephone conversation with my mother who told me she had bumped into Dr Lee in Oxford who had asked after my health and told her that, once the methods had developed further, a heart and lung transplant would be the answer. I was furious, turning yet again into my stubborn six-year-old self, feeling that any discussion of my health behind my back was not on and dismissed a transplant as, simply, not for me. But, once suggested, the idea followed me around for the coming years and I took note, against my will, of what was happening in the area of transplant medicine.

I had always been interested in cardiology and, in common with many other people with congenital heart problems, frequently knew more about my condition than the doctors I was seeing. It was rare and unusual – at least, as one doctor I saw told me, 'It's unusual to see any of you still alive at your age.' Well, I was certainly not dead yet and in the absence of other people's understanding, tried to be a walking encyclopaedia on Eisenmenger syndrome. The father of a schoolfriend was a cardiac surgeon, one of the first to successfully replace human heart valves with those from pigs in 1962. My friend Peta and I discussed this awesome and disgusting fact, that bits of pig could be put inside us – would we oink and snort like a pig, smell like a pig? It was the first time that it entered my consciousness that problems with hearts could be fixed.

In December 1967, Christiaan Barnard performed the first successful heart transplant, starting off what has now become a routine and effective medical treatment. In the 1960s, it was a different story. Transplantation had been around since the 1950s with mixed success. The first human kidney transplant, between identical twins, was performed in 1954, the recipient living eight years with his brother's kidney. In the following decade, researchers looked at the viability of other organ transplants, experimenting with transplanting hearts using animals. The first human who was, in essence, experimented on in Groote Schuur Hospital in Cape Town, South Africa, was fifty-five-year-old Louis Washkansky. Mr Washkansky was dying from severe heart failure – his heart was extremely enlarged and barely beating, with obstructions in his coronary arteries and heart wall caused by repeated heart attacks. He agreed, reportedly without hesitation, to receive a transplant and went on to live for eighteen days with his new heart, donated by a twenty-five-year-old, Denise Darvall, fatally injured in a road-traffic accident. While the heart transplant was successful, less was known then about the need to strike a balance between suppressing the immune system to prevent rejection, while at the same time preventing infection: and Mr Washkansky died from pneumonia caused by the immunosuppressant medication he was given.

Mr Washkansky was given eighteen more days of life with his new heart; nowadays, people are surviving over twenty years with new organs. Knowing what I now know about what a transplant is like, what a huge onslaught to the body such surgery is, I wonder about Mr

Washkansky and how he chose to spend the last few days of his life. If he had known that the transplant would only give him eighteen days of life, would he have chosen to die in peace? Or, regardless of how long he would live, would he still have chosen to go ahead with the pioneering operation and die famous?

I had watched the developments in transplantation over the years with mixed feelings and had decided, categorically, that it was not for me. As a result of taking part in experiments on rats during my psychology degree, I had been ardently against animal experimentation ever since. Influenced by books such as Peter Singer's *Animal Liberation* and Mary Midgley's *Animals and Why they Matter*, I became a vegetarian, at times a vegan, and insisted everyone else should be one too, until I developed malnutrition. I became known as the 'omelette bore', and was not popular at dinner parties. On one particularly bad day, I went into a shoe-shop and asked if they had any leather shoes made from animals that had died of natural causes. I did not like the idea of having anything to do with medications tested on animals, which ruled out most of them. And transplants were expensive: much better, according to my utilitarian, simplistic view of the world, that the money that went on one transplant were used instead to improve treatment of the elderly, or people with mental-health problems. Instead of one of me surviving, twenty, thirty, or forty elderly people could have their hip operations or receive better care in their old age.

Beside all that, I am a coward. Despite, or perhaps because of, a life filled with medical investigations, anything to do with hospitals filled me with dread. I hated the plastic smell of oxygen masks, the sound of trolleys on lino floors, the sight of blood. I hated pain, was the worst coward when it came to dentists or injections; hated being out of control; hated the routine of hospitals, not sleeping in my own bed, eating what I wanted to eat and when I wanted to, hated everything to do with being a patient. I put this in the past tense, because now, things are different. But in 2000, I hated the grinding boredom of illness. I was impatient, wanted to be better, to get on. The thought of being cut open horrified me. Let alone having people rooting around inside. And I knew, by then, far too much about the limitations of medicine, the potential for error, medical mistakes of omission and commission. So, no, a transplant was not for me. Or so I thought for the first forty or so years of my life. But when it comes to a matter of life or death, life puts up the bigger fight.

In fact, it was not just life-and-death issues that changed my mind. It was far more to do with my quality of life. I wanted to stay alive, yes, but not at any cost. I didn't want to die, but not just for me, but because of the impact on other people. Mo, my family. Especially my mother. I did not want to die before her. I hate the idea of burying her, but far more, I do not want her burying me. She has carried around the responsibility for my health since my birth; although not in any way her fault, she still feels responsible. I simply have to outlive her.

Apart from that, I loved my life in many ways. If I had been able to breathe, life would have been just fine. I was and still am, happily married. I met Mo (short for Malcolm) in 1991, at a party given by his ex, which I went to while disentangling myself from my first short marriage. I was sitting on the floor at the top of the stairs, wearing, I am not sure why, a very short skirt and blue-and-black patterned tights, and the first thing Mo saw when he walked up the stairs was my legs, which, he tells me, clinched things for him. His legs, unbeknown to him then, also clinched things for me – I had admired them a couple of years earlier, sticking out from underneath a motorbike he was fixing at the side of the road, just around the corner from where I was living in Oxford. The owners of the respective pairs of legs turned out to be compatible in other ways, and we have been together since then. Mo has always managed my health without any fuss, taking it into account without making any more of it than necessary. He has encouraged me to keep going and do as much as possible without being overly concerned. He has got the balance just right between looking after me because of my health needs and treating me just like anyone else. In short, not making me into a cripple. He seemed to enjoy walking at my pace, taking life slowly and admiring the view as we went; he carried on walking slowly even after my transplant, much to my annoyance when I wanted to charge ahead and flex my new muscles and I realised that he had not been loitering along simply to humour me.

As well as having Mo to live for, I have a big family which, despite all our differences and arguments, has got stronger and closer over the years. My friends too, and my work, I have always appreciated and enjoyed. All these things made my life, for me, just right. The advent of the lottery in 1994 started conversations about how our respective lives would change with all that money. I realised then that I would only want to change the one thing that a lottery win could not guarantee, my health. I just wanted to be able to breathe. If I could do that then I could carry on doing all the things I liked, see all the people I loved. I could walk, run, whatever I wanted; I could help other people for a change, rather than me always being the weaker one. During my schooldays, when 'excused' from games lessons, I did my homework in the school dining-room where the dinner ladies would take pity on me and make me a cup of tea. I liked it watery with lots of milk, rather than stand-your-spoon-up institutional brew. One of the women would see me coming and proclaim, 'Ooh, there's the weak one.' That was just was how I was now feeling. The weak one.

That's why I agreed to go to Papworth Hospital for an assessment for a heart and lung transplant.

4. The Quick-Fitters

September 2000–May 2001

A LETTER ARRIVED FROM Papworth. Cream paper, friendly words, a leaflet *Your Assessment*. Details of what to bring: nightwear, washbag, slippers, toothpaste. A three-night stay, lots of tests, lots of talking. The opportunity to meet other people who had had transplants. More tests, more talking.

I felt sick. A transplant. Me? How would I survive three nights in hospital? I went to the assessment in September armed with my new nightwear, new slippers and new tube of toothpaste. Mountains of books, sewing, radio, tapes, make-up, perfume.

Papworth seemed to me the most depressing place on earth, a building-site in the middle of fenland, ten miles east of Cambridge. Papworth was originally a pioneering hospital and community for treating tuberculosis. It was founded in 1918 by Pendrill Varrier-Jones (1883–1941), a Welshman with sultry good looks, devoted to giving the significant number (at that time) of people with TB not only a better chance of survival, but a better quality of life, a treatment philosophy echoed in that of the transplant unit nearly a century later. Varrier-Jones established a 'colony' of tubercular sufferers in Papworth Hall, now a grade-II-listed stately home in the middle of the hospital grounds. The patients built their own wooden shelters around Papworth Hall, small Wendy Houses open to the elements (to provide the inmates with the fresh air necessary for their treatment), and worked at various professions such as carpentry, printing or furniture-making during their recovery. A village settlement was built around the hospital to house the convalescent patients and their families, Varrier-Jones aiming to provide a complete model of treatment and aftercare for TB sufferers. He was ahead of his time in many ways, a pioneer and a good model for what was to follow. Once tuberculosis virtually disappeared with the advent of inoculation, Papworth continued as a centre for cardiothoracic surgery, Sir Terence English performing the UK's first successful heart transplant there in 1979. Although the tuberculosis hospital and sanatorium was originally in Papworth Hall, new ward blocks were built in the grounds in the 1920s around a large duck-pond, the wards opening onto wide verandas where beds were moved for open-air therapy. Today, patients use the verandas to sneak a quick smoke and make mobile-phone calls. On 26th September 2000 I was admitted to one of these blocks and had sufficient stamina, just, to slowly walk the length of the veranda while exploring my surroundings.

We had spent the previous night in a local hotel, an uncomfortable restless night fighting bedsprings and inner demons. I knew nothing about the hospital's history when we first arrived, otherwise I might have been more interested in the architecture, might have noticed the extensive landscaped grounds surrounding Papworth Hall. All I could see at 8 am that morning was a jumble of old and new and the chaos of a building-site. I did not want to be there and was beginning to feel like my six-year-old shadow. When we got to the ward the sun began to shine. The nurses gave a warm welcome, as did the two women sharing my room opening onto the veranda. Helen, the transplant coordinator, came to find us and went through my programme which began with a thorough going-over by one of the doctors.

The next couple of days were filled with tests and talk interspersed with stretches of boredom, when Mo and I wandered in the grounds, did jigsaws and read. I met the transplant nurses who told me about the medication required after a transplant. The more I heard, the more I decided this was not for me. Drugs to suppress my immune system. Drugs to suppress the side-effects of suppressing my immune system. Drugs to suppress the side-effects of the drugs to suppress the side-effects of the drugs to suppress the immune system. And more to suppress the side-effects of these. I heard about the risks: increased chances of getting cancer, high blood pressure, high cholesterol; a fat face and thin bones from steroids. Nausea and vomiting. Shaking. Mood swings, paranoia. Melancholy, melanoma. I beamed out, not able to believe that I was going to do this. Then more tests: chest X-rays, lung function.

My lung function was so poor that I scared the young technician doing the test. I had to walk up and down the corridor as fast as possible, wearing a device to measure the oxygen saturation of my blood. As I walked, my saturation fell to a level where the technician stopped the test, looking pale.

'I'm sorry, we are not allowed to carry on with measurements like this. We can't let you carry on below 50 per cent. It's not –'

'Healthy?' I tried to help him out.

'Well, it's not usual. Usually people are –'

'Dead?' Possibly not the right thing to say in such surroundings.

'Well, let's say such low levels don't usually sustain life.'

He looked embarrassed, uncertain of what to do. I wanted to put him out of his misery.

'I'm fine, I won't drop dead on you, I promise. It is normal, that's what happens, I'm adapted to it.'

'Yes, I see. But I'm not allowed to go on.'

My last chat was with the transplant consultant, a tall Australian Nicholas Cage lookalike. He folded himself into a chair and overcame the problem of his legs not fitting under the desk by using it as a foot-prop. Keith McNeil knew his stuff, knew a lot about Eisenmenger syndrome, was very positive about transplants and what one could do for me.

'It's all about quality of life,' he told me. 'Not length. A transplant will not make you live longer, but what you have will be better.'

He explained more. 'A transplant is, metaphorically, for Christmas, not for life. What it can give is some time of much better quality of life, being able to breathe, move, exercise normally. But it does not last for ever. There are problems all along the way. Rejection is an ongoing process, leading to steady damage of the new organs. The immunosuppressants increase the risk of serious infections and have long term side-effects.' He told me the survival statistics. 'Around 75 to 90 per cent chance of surviving two years after the operation. The rate steadily falls after that to less than 40 to 50 per cent five-year survival.' In other words, about half of those who have a transplant can expect to be alive after five years. Not brilliant, but what was my alternative?

'And without the transplant?' I asked Dr McNeil. It was to me the million dollar question. I had never really asked it before, just picked up the whispers.

'Well, it is all downhill from here. Today is the best day of the rest of your life. You know the score, it is a steadily deteriorating condition. You won't die tomorrow, unless you get knocked over by a bus. But your life will gradually get less and less fun.' I felt very relieved, reassured, talking to Keith. He talked my language, was honest, blunt. I needed to know what would happen and he told me. I was to hear this message several times more before the transplant.

'So,' I asked him, 'no telegrams from the Queen?'

He shook his head.

'With or without a transplant, I guess,' I said.

'Without, no. With, still unlikely.' I knew the score all right. This was about quality of life, not living to a hundred.

'But this is all theoretical at the moment,' Keith went on. 'We can definitely offer you a transplant, there's nothing that says otherwise. But, now, you're too well. You're still working, doing exercise, able to walk. Come back in five years and we'll see how things are then.'

So, by the end of September 2000, I had five more years before needing a transplant. I wanted to keep going as long as possible. Maybe. I did not want to think about it any more. I went back to work, carried on swimming, working, carried on with the routines of life. I had five years.

It was only five months.

*　　　　*　　　　*

By the beginning of 2001, my difficulties in breathing and chronic tiredness were such that people began to comment. My workplace, a decrepit Victorian asylum, now a supposedly modern psychiatric hospital, posed a series of insurmountable obstacles. Getting from the car into the psychology department was a major achievement – a walk of about a hundred yards requiring pre-planning, energy, time to recover at the other end to avoid people seeing me gasping in the corridor. Then they would ask me if I was all right, and I did not have the breath to answer. I would potter in, trying to look nonchalantly relaxed, and disappear into the conveniently sited Ladies next to the front door to catch my breath. At the end of the day, the routine would be reversed. Getting food was more of a problem. The canteen was up the sort of flight of stairs to be found in Victorian asylums: tall elegant ceilings meaning tall steep staircases. The stairs provided convenient resting places – at the top of one set of stairs people would stop and chat so I could stop and pretend to be waiting for someone. Then up the next set was a noticeboard, where I could stop and feign fascination at the cards inviting me to share a house with three quiet nurses or receive a free trial of colonic irrigation. Having caught my breath, only a few steps to go and if I had timed it right, I could then rest a few minutes in the queue for food. Then there came the day when I really could not make it up to the first stopping-point without feeling faint and people did stop and check up on me.

Why was it so important not to be noticed, not to attract attention? I couldn't bear, could never abide, kindly looks and words or pity or concern. I was all right. Really. This was something I knew about, nothing new, nothing unexpected. I was managing, coping, dealing with it. Not a problem. But of course, it was a great problem. Who on earth thought of putting the staff canteen up such a completely unmanageable staircase, rather than thinking through the needs of less than able-bodied staff and moving the canteen to the ground floor, or installing a lift? The tirade bubbled inside, waiting to erupt at some poor unsuspecting enquirer as to my well-being. And when I finally got to the top, finally made it to the top of the mountain, completed my epic journey around which my work day revolved, the food was crap. Complete and utter rubbish. Hospital bloody food.

It was so much easier to get cross about the food, the staircase than express the terror, helplessness, beginning to build up inside me. What was going to happen to me? There were many times when I got to the first resting-point on the stairs, warming my hands on the antique radiator while waiting for my chest to stop heaving, that I wanted to bawl my eyes out. One sympathetic look or word, I would have grabbed that person and howled. Please make it better. I can't do this any more. I am so sick of having to struggle like this. I just want to stop.

I would not let myself stop. I was determined to keep going as long as possible, whatever that took. I did not feel well, but when stationary, calm and tranquil in the face of stress, life was almost manageable. But, of course, it was not. Not really, looking back on it. But I liked to think at the time I was managing. I took on another book to write, on anxiety problems, confident that I could complete it without too much trouble. I partied over Christmas, laughed with friends, enjoyed time with family. A good act all things considered. I was definitely, noticeably bluer – people would remark on the colour of my fingers, toes. In the swimming-pool I would turn deep purple, attracting comments.

My mother, amongst others, told me repeatedly to take it easy, slow down, rest. It was not that I ignored her exactly, because I was beginning to need and respect perhaps for the first time her kindness and deep concern for my health which had been with me throughout my life. It had been in many ways helpful to stride off regardless. Neither my mother nor my cardiologist would have approved of potholing and squash at university, which was after all the point. Doing more than I should have gave me strength and confidence that I could be fit and healthy after all. But, this last few months before stopping, I began to crave her concern and almost want her to tell me to stop so I could for once be a dutiful daughter. Old habits die hard and even when she tried, I came up with all the usual justifications for keeping going: I'm managing; I love my work; they need me; I have responsibilities.

While those close to me were telling me to stop, the doctors, unsure about what was going on, were giving me an ambiguous message. I had three viral infections in a row and never picked up afterwards. I felt so unwell one weekend that I called the GP's deputy service. The tired doctor who arrived was taking no chances. 'You need to be in hospital,' he told me after taking a cursory look. In the medical admissions ward I was investigated for a pulmonary embolism. A rather nasty little test, injecting a dye through an arm vein to show up the vessels in the lungs, giving the overpowering sensation of having wet oneself. The registrar who looked at the film gave me the all-clear and I was sent home. On closer inspection a couple of weeks later, a large embolus could be seen hovering at the base of the pulmonary veins, which – had it become dislodged – would have done untold damage. But since none of us knew about it at the time, it was not a problem. Before I went home that day, the consultant on the ward said my tiredness and breathlessness were probably related to the viral infections and, he said, 'could be got over with a spot of moral grit.' Had I not been so exhausted and wan, I would have told him where to put his moral grit, a diet I had been living on all my life.

But moral grit it was. I marched on. Until the last day. What I needed was a knight in shining armour to scoop me away from it all, with my head lolling gracefully, hair streaming out behind as I was rushed to safety. My rescuer came from an unlikely source. One of my own patients, a nurse, made a concerned comment to me during a therapy session indicating that she did not think I looked up to the job of looking after her at the moment. Her comment brought me up short. I could not carry on pretending.

The next day I parked my car the usual hundred yards from the department and started my marathon towards the door. I got a few steps and had to stop, gasping, exhausted. I waited and waited for my breath to return. It took ten minutes. I pretended to look through my bag, looking for lost keys. I walked a few more steps, slowly, slowly and inched into work. I was teaching that day, all day – somehow I had not had the courage to cancel, to say no. I would, after all, be sitting down all day, talking, I knew what to say, I had done it before, I had it all planned. I put on my Brave Face. Cheerful, joking, chatty, knowledgeable. A good performance. Only for the fact that I was gasping for breath. And this time it was very noticeable. I saw a few puzzled looks, concerned faces. But somehow I got through the day. I talked less and less, asked the students to work on their own while I recovered. I heard later that one of the participants had put down my breathlessness to being nervous. I wasn't nervous, I was terrified. By now everyone else was worried too. My GP, whom I called when I got home, was sufficiently worried to admit me to hospital. And the hospital was sufficiently worried to keep me there for two weeks. And I was, in turn, sufficiently worried not to argue. I knew, then, that the pretending was over.

*   *   *

When I finally ended up in hospital in Oxford on 1st May 2001 I had a lot of learning to do. On the cardiology ward, I experienced for the first time a deep gratitude and relief to hand over control to the medics. I arrived and lay on my bed for a couple of hours waiting for the doctors to come and have their chat. I realised that there was nowhere else in the world I would rather be. I could, at last, just stop. No more pretending, no more struggle. I could be tired, breathless, unable to walk very far, and everyone understood. I did not have to explain, make excuses and jokes. I could just be highly disabled by what was by now a completely buggered-up cardiovascular system.

My clinical signs could match my diagnosis. I relaxed into being a patient with Eisenmenger syndrome, severe pulmonary hypertension, severe cyanosis. I was brought a cup of tea, helped up into a sitting position to drink it. The nurses would not let me walk to the toilet, but wheeled me there after my refusal to use a commode. I rested. I did, for the first time in my life, nothing. I did not try at all. And it was wonderful.

I was on the ward for two weeks, changing my mind from thinking that I had five years to go, to believing that a transplant may be imminent. I struggled to get my head round it all. What does it mean … who am I if I can't work or carry on as normal? Am I ready to face death? Am I ready for a transplant and all that it entails? And will I still be me if I have someone else's organs inside me?

The subject of the transplant was carefully and sensitively handled by my cardiac team who introduced the idea slowly, performing tests to rule out any other treatable possibilities for the breathlessness such as endocarditis or infection. They realised that I was not quite ready to take the plunge towards the transplant door and that I would fight on until it really was the last resort. All their good work was swept aside one Saturday morning when the duty cardiologist, graced with good looks but not tact, announced from round the curtains: 'So, there is nothing much we can do for you here, the whole lot is going to have to come out. You're the transplant lady, aren't you?'

I was outraged. No one so far had been so blunt and no, I was not ready quite then to take on such information. I cried that night. One is not supposed to cry in hospital, but I needed to, so just got on with it, trying to get enough sobs out before the nurse rushed in to mop me up. I was not even sure what I was crying about. Maybe not being able to go to the swimming-pool or to work; maybe the black hole that had appeared before me; maybe missing Mo's body in the bed. In the way that tears shift things, something shifted and new possibilities began to emerge. Just say, I thought, I did have a transplant – and say, perhaps, tentatively, hopefully, it was a success – then I would be able to do anything that I wanted to do. I'd be able to walk, for a start, swim without gasping and turning blue, dance without stopping. It seemed far too dangerous to look fully at these possibilities that night, but a quick glimpse was enough to begin to change my perception. The image of these possibilities was what kept me going for the next long stretch of months, over a year, but just then I needed a quick glimpse.

In hospital, I stabilised. That is what they called it. I think, really, I calmed down. Settled in to it all. Relaxed into the role of sickness, disability. Slowed down, accepted help, asked for what I needed rather than struggling to do it myself. I talked to other patients and realised that I seemed, unexpectedly, to hold a trump card. In the patient's sitting room in the evening, we would all gather, me with my oxygen cylinder, and a selection of middle-aged men with open-front pyjamas, some with scarred chests, often large, flabby. They would compare notes. 'A bypass tomorrow, I'm terrified.' 'I have to have an angiogram, not very nice. I wish I'd never smoked.' The usual moans about the food, the cleaning or lack of. It would be my turn. 'Why are you here, love?' 'Well, actually, I have to have a heart and lung transplant.' There would be a stunned silence, a sharp intake of breath, then 'Blimey. You look so young. What are we all complaining about?' What indeed. Then a long interrogation. 'Will they do it here? When's the operation? Why do you need it? How will you be afterwards?' No one ever asked me how I felt.

Before leaving hospital, I prepared for my new life. I was to go to Papworth to talk further about the transplant. Meanwhile, I had to be on oxygen most of the day and all night. I left hospital with, as well as the regulation square bag of drugs, a mountain of black-and-white oxygen tanks and several miles of green tubing so we could trail oxygen around the house. Not to mention a bellyful of relief and a glimmer of hope. I was, from now on, disabled.

5. Tragic but Brave

May–October 2001

I GUESS I HAD BEEN DISABLED, un-abled, non-able-bodied for quite some time, but not willing or able to admit it to myself. I'd spent my life trying to be as normal as possible, trying to keep up with the able bodied, physically fit, pink people. Trying to keep up with the grown-ups. And now I was disabled. Physically challenged, physically limited. The terms are meaningless, really. After all, many of us are disabled in some or other aspect of life. Too physically unfit to walk up the stairs in Marks and Spencer. People unable to get out of the house because of agoraphobia; or the many carrying inner scars from trauma and abuse, the disabilities not being immediately apparent but easily triggered. Disabled people, the real disabled people, have to look the part – one or no legs; sitting in a wheelchair; crutches; bowed spine. I wasn't one of these, clearly, but for years could not really get myself around without enormous effort. My only concession had been to get a disabled-parking badge which attracted dirty looks from elderly drivers struggling to get their wheelchairs from the back of the cars. I looked healthy, or so everyone kept on telling me. Because of the cyanosis, I, in common with other people with Eisenmenger syndrome, looked dusky pink, suspiciously like the glow following the gym, only visible as a different colour to the practised eye. I turned out well, I made an effort to scrub up every day – make up, matching bra and knickers, jewellery. I didn't look like a cripple. But I was.

47

People with congenital heart conditions have what might be called 'hidden disabilities.' It is not immediately apparent why they struggle through life, get exhausted, take time off work or don't work at all, refuse to lift heavy bags or walk up hills. We might be a bunch of malingerers, lazy sods, to all intents and purposes. People cannot see why we stop when we feel tired, lacking any reserve of energy to keep going. My lack of reserve got me into no end of trouble when I would bite off more than I could chew. One summer a few years earlier, Mo and I had gone to Scotland for a holiday. We set out for a walk on Iona, a tiny island off Mull, windswept heather, easy to walk around in an afternoon, or so the guidebook said. The book did not allow for the weather changing, or for finding out that my waterproof jacket was not as advertised. I got soaked and suddenly hit my limit. I could not go on. We were not really in any danger. From the top of the hill we were standing at the bottom of, we could have seen the island's port and we were only half an hour's walk away from the road. But I simply could not go on. My limbs seized up, I could not breathe. Mo encouraged, exhorted, I tried and fell over, gasping. As much as I told my limbs to move, beseeched my fighting spirit to get to work, nothing happened. Exasperated, Mo stuck me on his back and marched up the hill, me bemoaning my pathetic heart, him bemoaning my confidence in setting out for the walk in the first place. Somehow we made it back to the village, soaked, and I crawled into bed for the next couple of days to recuperate.

This lack of reserve is universal. Val, who had valve problems, described it as 'like someone's pulled out the plug. That's it. Empty. Tiredness like nothing else.' Val is my friend Jane's mother and one of the first people I met who also had a heart condition. She, like me, is stubborn. Unlike me, she went on to have three children against medical advice. She knows that people don't understand. When I went to my first meeting of the patients' association GUCH (Grown-Up Congenital Hearts), I met people like me and we all had one thing in common: stroppyness. We had to state our case, hold our ground, assert our needs. If we didn't do it, no one else did. The world is not designed for people with half hearts.

I went home from hospital in May 2001 for my new life as one of the real disabled, a tragic but brave sufferer, the object of people's stares and pity. We had to get organised. We were supplied with oxygen concentrators, small machines a bit like an astromech droid, R2-D2, that chug away in the corner of a room removing nitrogen from the air and blowing out pure oxygen through tubes running around the house. I got used to wearing a nasal cannula. Not the most sartorially pleasing fashion accessory, the tube loops around the ears and under the chin, with two dainty little horns to push into the nostrils, causing a permanently runny and sore nose. Occasionally the trailing tube would get caught on something as I passed, causing the prongs to be jettisoned out of my nose at speed, whirling around the room, accompanied by sprays of snot and Vaseline. We had a supply of oxygen tanks of differing sizes – a large one for the car where I would sit puffing away, pulling faces to inquisitive children while waiting at traffic-lights, and small tanks for when we went on outings. Friends would come around to have a go with the oxygen, seeing if it gave them a buzz. The neighbours brought their ancient cat around to be revived by my oxygen when he was facing his final days.

We entered the world of stair lift salesmen, who would offer condolences, sympathy, then settle in for the hard sell. 'Ours have all the safety straps. Just think how awful it would be if you fell off when the chair was still moving and you got stuck behind it. We can guarantee that that won't happen.' I pointed out that I could guarantee that it wouldn't happen without all the safety straps, since it would be quite difficult for me to fall off a chair moving at about one metre per minute unless drunk. We settled, in the end, for a jolly chap called Dave who did a lot of work for council homes, who was far more interested in finding out the gory details of transplants than in selling me a chairlift.

'It's completely basic,' he told me. 'Looks horrible, plastic seat, you won't need any safety-belts. We can fit you a second-hand one so long as it is in stock and we'll buy it back from you when you're better. Can fit it in a couple of days if I can get someone to look after the kids.'

Dave, true to his word, fitted a cheap, basic and ugly chairlift in a couple of days. It revolutionised my life. I could get upstairs with no effort. I could also carry a load of washing, tray of tea on my lap. Even the cats enjoyed riding up and down. My nephews gave it the thumbs up: 'That's really co-ool,' and a friend's small child insisted they get one too.

And, of course, the wheelchair. The Red Cross lent us a fold-up canvas wheelchair with rubber tyres, designed to be as ergonomically unsound as possible, with wheels just the right size to make getting up and down kerbs a technological impossibility without precarious tilting. But have wheels, can travel. I discovered the delights of effortless movement. All I had to do was shout my commands and off we would go. Mo rose to the challenge like a true natural, whizzing me round corners, chucking me effortlessly on and off curbs, causing pedestrians to leap aside when they saw us coming. We perfected the one-wheel turn. We soon learned that wheelchairs are not designed for cross-country use when I ended up stuck in mud, half-way up a hill in the University arboretum. We tried to get out of there fast, leaving deep tyre treads just in front of the 'Keep off the Grass' sign.

I realised, sitting attached to an oxygen cylinder in a wheelchair with someone to look after me, that as a member of the 'real disabled' I had certain privileges. Rather than people coming up behind me and tut-tutting at my extremely slow pace of walking, they would slow down and pass with reverent, embarrassed respect, in the way of passing a hearse. In clothes shops, assistants would run around and fetch me things, rather than me having to struggle to find different sizes. I could legitimately use lifts without getting dirty looks from pram-pushers. Children, finding someone down at their level, would initiate conversation as though I was an old friend. Most kids were chatty. 'I'm having a party – I'm six today, but I'm not inviting Thomas,' one little boy told me. 'Why's that?' I asked him. 'Thomas is a cat. He doesn't like parties,' he replied, solemnly. I was firmly put in my place by a young girl who, finding me at eye level, looked at me accusingly and demanded '*Why* are you in a *pushchair*?'

With the oxygen, stair lift and wheelchair, we were organised. Bunkered in for a long haul. But where to now? I had to make some decisions about my future: to stay disabled or go for a transplant. We went back to Papworth for another chat, this time with a commitment from me to seriously consider the possibility of going ahead with the operation. We met up again with Helen, the transplant coordinator, to talk through what was involved. I heard once more the message that a transplant aimed to give me a better quality rather than length of life. I learned more about the operation – I'd be in hospital for about three weeks if everything went well, then would be discharged to a flat in the hospital grounds to begin to live independently before going home. I would learn to manage all the medication and how to do daily checks to monitor signs of rejection. The average wait for a transplant was nine to eighteen months, depending on whether donor organs were available – it could be a wait of one day, or years. I saw Dr McNeil, still as tall, still as laid-back, who told me of the risks.

'I'd say you've got an 80 to 90 per cent chance of surviving the operation,' he told me. That was good news, but I would have preferred to hear the words one hundred.

'Does it ever go completely wrong, so I would end up much more disabled?' Val had a valve replacement operation several years before and had a stroke after the operation, leaving her severely limited. It had made me think twice about surgery and I needed to know.

'No, you either get through it or you don't. If you survive the surgery, the first couple of weeks, then the next six months, then you've got a good chance of doing well.'

'And how long does it take to get over it all? Get back to work?'

'I've had patients go back to work two weeks after a transplant. I had one who was a triathlete, entering competitions six months later.'

Helen was more cautious, but still optimistic. 'It's about three to six months if everything goes well.'

The Papworth staff were upbeat, positive, optimistic. They spoke of the benefits of a transplant. I would be able to exercise, live a normal life. Play sports, go dancing. Anything. I had to be careful about infection, take the medication, do the monitoring, but otherwise could have a normal life. But there were no guarantees about how long for, or what kind of problems I might face. And no one at Papworth would give me firm advice about whether, or when, to go ahead. That was my decision. Dr McNeil had been impartial. 'We cannot advise you,' he told me when I asked his opinion. 'All we can do is give you the information and let you decide. You need to decide whether your life is so unbearable as it is that you are willing to take the risks of the operation in the hope of getting something better. But, it's your life. Your decision. It's up to you.' I had to take the responsibility for the decision, 100 per cent. No one could tell me what to do.

The surgeon I spoke to was equally honest.

'Each transplant is the first of its kind,' he said. 'Each is a new experiment, things are constantly changing. It's difficult to make predictions. We're at the cutting edge here.' I tried not to laugh nervously, although he had not seen the joke. I was talking to Mr Dunning at the end of my visit, the end of the day. He looked tired, distracted, but he was warm, likable. I looked closely at his hands to detect any signs of shaking. Suppressed a thought about where those hands had been. I asked about the operation, what it was like.

'Well, it's not like having your toenails cut,' he told me. 'You'll feel pretty messed up afterwards.' I was not sure what this meant, but left it at that. Of course it would be difficult, rough, traumatic. The aspect I did not want to think about. I asked for Mr Dunning's opinion – what would your advice be, should I go ahead or not? He was more encouraging than other people I'd spoken to.

'If you are going to go ahead, don't leave it too long. The healthier you are when we operate, the better you are likely to do. You look in good shape at the moment.' Only a transplant surgeon is allowed to greedily eye a woman's chest, looking for the shape of the sternum, the robustness of the surrounding body. I bumped into Dr McNeil again just before we left Papworth and told him that Mr Dunning was encouraging of me going ahead sooner rather than later.

'Ah,' Dr McNeil replied, 'surgeons like to do surgery.'

We needed time to think. Balance up the risks – the risks of surgery versus the risks of waiting. The benefits of surgery versus the benefits of doing nothing, letting nature take its course. My fate was in my hands.

I knew that my family, friends, would be anxious to know what was decided at Papworth, assuming perhaps that we would be guided to a definite decision. We asked in advance to be given some space and time to think on our own, a request which was honoured. I knew that my parents would find this very difficult. Since being ill I had spent more time with my father than ever before. He came over for coffee, told me about his childhood, his work as a physicist during the war. We talked, perhaps really talked for the first time. But we only very occasionally spoke about the transplant. He was always optimistic, refusing to believe that there could be other than a positive outcome. Once when I asked him how he managed to be so positive about the whole thing, he told me, 'Sometimes, if I really think about it, I feel like I'm shaking inside. My way is to deal with bad things when they happen. Otherwise I don't think about them. That's just my way. Your mother does the worrying in advance.' That was the closest we ever got to a discussion of emotional matters. On one occasion he said he thought that having a transplant was the best possible thing to do.

'But you can't say that, Dad,' I replied. 'What if you advised me to go ahead and I died during the operation, how would you feel then?' He never tried to influence me after that and respected our need for time. My mother, too, remained quiet, offering only practical help during these days, but I can only try to imagine what was going on for her. She'd been with me throughout all my hospital treatments as a child and now I had asked to be left alone.

So, we thought, we discussed, we ruminated. How bad was life now? I was tethered to an oxygen machine most of the day and night, despite which I became breathless very quickly. I felt exhausted most of the time, needed help with getting dressed, getting ready for bed on bad days. I could not go out on my own, needed a wheelchair to go any distance. Not a happy picture. On the other hand, part of me still believed that with a bit of moral fibre, more fighting spirit, if I could only *try* harder, I could perhaps get back to where I was before – struggling, but still able to enjoy a reasonable if limited life. Mo looked incredulous when I told him what I believed. 'It's just not going to happen,' he emphasised. 'Look at you. You try every day. You're still fighting. But things have changed. You cannot do it any more.'

We decided to give it time. Papworth had indicated that there was no hurry, I was not likely to drop dead suddenly. Things were declining, but at, hopefully, a slow rate.

Over the next couple of months we tried to normalise our new life. Although physically limited, my brain, having got over the shock of all the recent changes, needed exercise. I started to write and found that I could do a small amount each day. I had been learning Greek and picked up my books and tapes, reciting Greek numbers and requests for coffee, water, toilets, a doctor, a transplant, to impassive cats. Friends came to visit. We had a good summer. I could sit outside and read and write. Life settled into a rhythm, visitors, a bit of work, expeditions with the wheelchair and oxygen. I was sort of contented. Life felt much easier than it had been, no stress or strains. Just a huge decision as to whether to go ahead with something that might kill me.

In September, one lunchtime, having made all the effort of getting up and dressed, I decided to go back to bed again and watch a video. Although I could call myself ill, I never fitted comfortably into the sick role and most days I would try to have some sense of normality – getting up, doing some work, seeing someone, eating at normal times, doing a bit of domestic stuff, even if this was asking the cleaners to help out. But on this Tuesday, going back to bed seemed acceptable. I put the television on, ready to switch on the video, and watched a bit of an aeroplane disaster movie, a large plane crashing into the side of a tall building. Then for some reason the film was wound back and repeated and repeated. And moments later, another plane crashed into the neighbouring building. It took some time to distinguish reality from fiction. I realised these were live pictures from the Twin Towers in New York. My mouth fell open, literally, as mouths were, at that moment, falling open all over the world. I watched as the towers fell down, collapsing like ballasted buildings, falling in on themselves. I watched tiny dots falling from the buildings just before they started to collapse, dots I later realised were people.

A week later, still in my wheelchair, I took part in a demonstration in Oxford to voice my opposition to the threat of retaliatory action for the September 11th terrorist atrocities. Later I was to spend a freezing Saturday in February 2003, my scars from the transplant only just beginning to heal, shuffling through central London with a million other people protesting once more as Britain and America geared up towards war with Iraq. World events made my own difficulties seem trivial, insignificant. Something catastrophic can happen to anyone, anytime. It was a wake-up call. What am I waiting for? I've got a chance of life. Why not take it?

In October 2001 I saw my consultant in Oxford. Dr Gribbin had retired two years previously, much to my sadness, and was replaced by Adrian Banning, warm, humorous and not out of place on the rugby pitches. We talked about how I was coping. I cheerfully explained my book, Greek, going out, seeing people.

'It's almost too good,' Dr Banning said. 'You're coping too well. It has got to give sometime.' He went on to tell me about a patient who was waiting for a transplant in hospital. He was fine, cheerful, coping, optimistic until he finally got the call to say donor organs were available. At that point he went to pieces, was a wreck, terrified, clinging to the nurses. He needed to be anxious and for him the anxiety arrived all at once. I recalled research showing that patients who became anxious before surgery did much better than those who were completely calm, denying any fears, who tended to become much more anxious afterwards, not to know at that time just how true this was to prove for me. 'I do feel quite calm at the moment,' I told Dr Banning. 'But yes, I'm sure at some stage I'll fall to pieces. I'll let you know when I do.'

I explained my dilemma about the transplant. He knew me well by then, knew I was a fighter, knew my fears and reluctance to engage with medical treatments.

'You know I cannot give you advice,' he said, 'but you are very stoical. Most other people would be kicking and screaming, demanding something is done. There are thousands of people waiting for transplants, so if you are at all ambivalent, it makes sense that the transplant will go to someone else who is desperate for it.'

'But how do I know when I should be desperate? What about the risks?' I asked. He leaned back in his chair, pressed his fingertips together.

'If I was a friend, not Dr Banning, just a friend,' he said, carefully, 'I would say what are you waiting for? You're not going to get better. The transplant statistics are, what, a 70 per cent chance of being alive in two years. I'm not sure I can give you those odds without a transplant.'

'Okay, what are my odds? What will happen if I don't have the transplant?' My million dollar question, a little thought sneaking into my mind, 'Maybe he would tell me I don't really need it.'

'You will have a lot more problems with your heart, heart failure, your lungs filling up with fluid. You're likely to have to spend a lot of time in hospital. Or worse. It is not good.'

In other words, pull your finger out.

When I went out of the door, I felt something shift in my inner self. The prickly sensation arising from the answer to a long-elusive problem emerging into sharp focus. The next day I telephoned Papworth and asked to go on the list.

6. Life in the Corridor

October 2001 – June 2002

I SAT ON THE STAIRS to make the telephone call. I am not sure why. Sitting in a comfortable chair, poised, ready, relaxed, may have been more sensible, but for beginning the process of turning my life upside down, stairs seemed the better option. With stairs you can go either way, up or down.

We returned a couple of days later to Papworth, to run through the final stages before being 'listed'. More blood tests to check I had not contracted anything nasty in the last few months – with my dormant lifestyle, chance would be a fine thing. A few swabs to test whether I'd picked up anything during my stays in hospital, the MRSA bug becoming a serious problem. Helen, the transplant coordinator, took us into a quiet side-room to talk. I had lots of questions for her: would I be aware of being in intensive care? My images of intensive care were taken from television dramas, with the pale and intubated patient lying serenely, surrounded by bleeping, blinking machines and tubes, concerned relatives holding the inert patient's hand. Tragic but brave, indeed. No, Helen told me, I would not know much about it. Sometimes patients had to be taken back into theatre for problems with bleeding, but I would be unaware of this happening. Would I be in much pain? Again the answer was no – pain was well controlled with medication, morphine to begin with and later a combination of paracetamol and one or two other painkillers. People could experience discomfort from the chest-drains – chest-drains? What were these? Tubes to drain out excess fluid and air after the operation, located in my chest for about five days afterwards. Ah, this sounded like too much information, so I conveniently blocked it out, not knowing at the time that later, these chest drains were going to give me my main problems in recovering from the surgery.

I went on to more practical matters. When would I be up and about afterwards? About five days after the surgery when the chest-drains are taken out, I would go down to the gym to begin an exercise programme. Five days? I was amazed. Hospital dramas shows the patient lying wanly around for weeks, every need being catered for, before emerging pale but triumphant to return to full health. Nowadays, no patient is allowed to remain stationary for more than a few minutes, having to move and exercise as soon as possible to get everything back to normal and reduce the risk of thromboses. We discussed getting a bag ready for going into hospital at short notice, containing a complete survival kit. Nightwear, comfortable clothes for lying around in, slippers, toothpaste, towel. Books, money for the payphone. We had lists for Brownie camp at school – plastic mug, plate, knife, fork, spoon. Now, my hospital list included an eye-mask to shut out the inevitable lights that would stay on all night, earplugs, a radio.

All through the whole system there were no guarantees. I would be on a list to be called up at some time, from the day I was listed to two years or more afterwards or never. When I get the call, I may or may not have a transplant. Sometimes, calls are 'false alarms' where for some reason the transplant cannot go ahead, such as when there is something wrong with the donor organs or if the recipient has an infection. If it went ahead, I might not even survive the operation. If I survived the operation, I did not know how long I would then live. Or what quality of life I would have. I might get infections. I might get repeated rejection episodes. I might be in and out of hospital for a long time. I pondered these for a moment. I might well go mad if I think about all these possibilities. I might as well hope for the best. I might as well go on the list.

I went home clutching my pager, a back-up in case I was not contactable by telephone. Since nowadays we are never more than nine feet away from a telephone, a statistic which also applies to our hypothetical distance from a rat, it seemed that the pager was the least important tool of the transplant process, but to me it seemed highly significant.

We arrived back home on the Thursday evening and I had asked to go on the list at 10 am on Saturday, to allow time to gather together my pyjamas and toothpaste. On Friday I packed my bag and designed my funeral service. I wrote a list of my favourite music – Sting, Pachelbel's canon, Mozart's 'Vesperae', the 'Arrival of the Queen of Sheba'. I gave instructions to be cremated in a cardboard coffin to decrease pollution, my ashes to be used to plant a tree and for no one to wear black and everyone to enjoy a good party afterwards.

At 10 am on Saturday 13th October, I knew that I was on The List. If suitable organs were available I could be called for a transplant at any time. At 10.15 am on Saturday, I went to the bathroom and flung the pager down the toilet. I had clipped the pager on to my belt, as instructed, forgetting that it would fly off when I undid it. The pager landed in the thankfully clean toilet-bowl. A perfect, mistaken, shot. I was mortified. I rescued it and dried it out, trying to work out a suitable story to tell Papworth that I needed a replacement. I was out walking in the rain and it got wet. A likely story, given my walking was restricted to a few yards around the house. It was not working properly when I got home. I've never been very good at lying, the truth always being far more amusing than fiction, so realised that I would have to confess my clumsiness. I tested my pager later on and it seemed to be working. Later in the afternoon it started bleeping, a characteristic sequence of four lots of three beeps, getting louder and more insistent each time. Was this the water or a call for a transplant? Just in case and with shaking hands, I telephoned Papworth and spoke to Stephen, one of the coordinators on call over the weekend. 'No, sorry, it is not us calling you,' he said. 'The pager may be picking up some other frequencies – sometimes police signals can set them off.' Or water molecules, I added to myself.

We then settled down to life in the corridor, a long, narrow room where the doors to my previous life were firmly closed, locked. Other doors were ahead. Death while waiting for a transplant. Death during surgery. A successful transplant. The latter door was the brightest colour, had the shiniest handle and richly engraved nameplate, but the other doors, grey, dark, were hovering within sight. Meanwhile, my corridor had to be made as comfortable as possible.

That October, autumn arrived with a flourish, with weeks of sunshine and proud arboreal displays. Mo had a week off work and each day we went out. He walked, I sat, as he pushed me round parks and gardens, stately homes and museums. Blenheim Palace, Christ Church Meadows, Waddesdon Manor, tourists in our home town. We went out for lunches, teas, for as long as my oxygen cylinders would last. I could manage to be out for a couple of hours at a time, long enough to fill each day with colour, like a holiday. My pager came along too, a little presence that could not be easily forgotten. I felt settled in for a long wait, deciding that for me it would be at least a year – during which time my job was to keep as well and as sane as possible. The clocks changed at the end of the month, bringing to an end a long summer.

At the end of the month, too, Homebase decided to stay open until 10 pm and have a huge sale. At 9.30 pm Mo and Anthony decided to go and buy a ladder at a cut-price rate. At 9.32 pm Helen from Papworth telephoned.

'Hello Diana. We need you to come in. There is a possibility that a suitable donor is available. Just a possibility at this stage.' Helen sounded calm.

'I can't,' I replied. 'Mo's buying a ladder.'

Neither of us could really see the relevance of my comment, but it seemed more appropriate at the time than hysterical giggling and screams. I needed to be very calm. This was impossible, it was far too early. I was not ready. I ran up the stairs, only realising that I had done so when my heart strongly objected when I tried to pull my bag out of the bottom of the wardrobe. I sat down and tried to catch my breath and telephoned Annie next door. She came round, Very Calm. We both tried to be Very Calm. I telephoned Mo's mobile, which rang in the kitchen. I telephoned Homebase and spoke to a bored-sounding assistant, who thought I was joking when I asked him to make an announcement: 'Would Mo Chandler please return home as soon as possible, your wife is about to be driven up the M40 at speed by some man she has never met before in order to have her heart and lungs replaced.' Mo arrived back a few minutes later, Very Calm, with Anthony, whatever the opposite of very calm might be. Amongst mayhem and pandemonium, we organised Ann and Anthony to look after the cats – we may be away some time – got our bags organised and I put on my make up. It seemed, somehow, an appropriate thing to do. And we sat down and waited.

After half an hour turned into an hour and a half, we began to get concerned. Perhaps they had changed their minds. Perhaps it was all a joke. We telephoned and were told that the driver was on his way. A few minutes later the transport service phoned to say the driver would be with us shortly. By this time, we had nearly completed the *Radio Times* easy crossword, told each other that we loved each other, cuddled the cats and I had changed my clothes twice. Finally my driver arrived, Kyle, a jolly ex-navy Australian. The back roads to Papworth were flooded, so we would go via the motorways – M40, M25, A1. Mo decided to follow us in the car in order to have transport the other end. And we set off, blue light flashing, into a dark windy night.

At the same time that I was spinning up the motorways, chatting inanely to Kyle who was keen to get back to action in the Navy, events were unfolding elsewhere which might lead to my transplant that night. Somewhere else, possibly in the south east of the country, although not necessarily, someone had been declared brain dead, with all the trauma and pain that entailed. On top of facing the reality that the person will not survive, the relatives may well be asked if their husband, wife, child, parent, sibling, friend can donate organs to save another person's life. That day, someone's relatives, somewhere, had said yes.

People who donate organs for transplantation die from a variety of causes. One main cause used to be road-traffic accidents: ironically, since road-traffic accidents are a occupational hazard for transplant drivers. Improvements in road safety, starting with Jimmy Savile urging us to Clunk Click Every Trip in the 1970s, structural changes to make cars safer and speed regulations, along with advances in trauma medicine, mean that people are simply not dying the way they did. Which is good news for drivers and bad news for those needing transplants. Traumatic injury, sudden brain haemorrhage and other causes lead to early death and possible donation. Potential donors need to be cared for in an intensive care unit prior to death. Organs from people who have actually died, where the circulation has stopped for any length of time, cannot be used, since so much deterioration occurs after death that the organs cannot remain viable in a new body. If after, say, a sudden head injury or haemorrhage, the individual is rushed to hospital with a beating heart and circulation, but is then found to be brain dead, that person may potentially become an organ donor.

Once the relatives have given their permission for the organs to be donated, a sequence of events is set into motion. At the donor end, a transplant coordinator is responsible for ensuring that the organs are used appropriately and for looking after the donor family. The coordinator has to be both swift and efficient organiser and broker and compassionate carer. Once the donor's blood-group and essential details of tissue type are known, the donor coordinator sets about looking for a suitable recipient. Ideally, this should be as near as possible to the donor: so, if the donor dies in London or the South-East, Papworth will be contacted first. If no suitable recipient is available, the search goes wider, and in some cases Europe-wide. Most donors can donate several organs – heart, lungs, liver, kidneys, corneas, skin, pancreas – involving lots of communication with many potential recipients.

As soon as a potential recipient is found, he or she is contacted and asked to come into hospital; and at the transplant centre, the transplant team assemble just in case. In some cases and possibly in my case that October night, more than one recipient will be contacted. If my donor was found to have a viable heart, say, but something wrong with the lungs, then someone in need of just a heart transplant could be lined up; or conversely, the lungs but not the heart could be used, then potential single- or double-lung recipients would need to be on red alert. That night, I had no idea if I was the only one heading towards Papworth, or whether, as for those attending a party, people were converging from different directions.

At the same time that we were driving up the M25, at the donor end a team of doctors and nurses, known as 'harvesters', would be preparing the donor for surgery. A terrible, awesome surgery which ends, inevitably, with the cessation of the donor's life. The donor's body has to be kept on a ventilator to allow blood to circulate to the organs; but the person is, to all intents and purposes, dead, due to lack of brain activity. Only when the donor's organs are removed is it possible to say whether they are suitable for transplant. A seemingly healthy donor may be found to have problems only apparent on post-mortem examination, such as early signs of lung or heart disease. The organs may deteriorate while the individual is on a ventilator so they become unsuitable for transplant. More detailed blood-tests may reveal hidden problems. Which means that the process of transplantation can be halted at any stage, the so-called 'false alarms'.

That night, with all this activity going on somewhere else, I felt very calm. Completely calm, almost oblivious to what was going on, as though I was simply staring at a black wall. Kyle and I talked about our lives, politics, putting the world to rights. He told me, which I did not want to know, that, as well as transporting patients, he also drove organs from donor hospitals to transplant units. I sneaked a look in the back of the car to see if there was any tell-tale sealed box. I couldn't see one. When we got to Papworth at midnight, empty and quiet, Kyle wished me luck – the first mention of what might be ahead. Mo, who had arrived with our car, wheeled me into the transplant unit where we were met by Helen, who told us that they were not able to offer anything that night. This was a false alarm.

By this time, all I wanted was a cup of tea and to go home to bed, so I was not able to be disappointed. But I asked Helen who the donor was and was told it was a forty-five-year-old woman who had died of a brain haemorrhage. The same age as me. Here was I, rushing up the motorway, making polite conversation and somewhere else the lives of a family, children, parents, friends, were shattered. Our lives were not to be connected, but they might have been. I realised then what a transplant is all about: connecting the dead with the living. The pain one side, the possibilities the other.

The next day I thought about that forty-five-year-old woman, a sudden, early death and the complexity of the web each life weaves. I thought about the people who would be affected by her death, in the weeks, months and years to come. Her husband and children, perhaps even grandchildren. Brothers, sisters. Elderly parents, losing a daughter before their own deaths, in an insult to the grand scheme of things. Her neighbours, work colleagues. Closest friend. Old schoolfriend. Her hairdresser. The milkman. So many people are touched by a death. And it could have been me, with all the network of people in my life hearing about my death. What kind of impact would it have on them? Or, I could this morning be unconscious in intensive care, my bag stowed away next to some hospital bed. Benefiting from another death. Such huge issues, too much to think about when numb and exhausted from adrenaline and lack of sleep. I also felt a wave of disappointment. This could have been the end of the waiting and the beginning of the next phase. Like a prisoner told of freedom only to have it pulled away when walking out of the cell, I had to go on with life in the corridor and get on with it. I knew for the first time that I had made the right decision. I wanted to go ahead with the transplant, whatever the risks and costs to me. I just had to go on waiting.

So we waited. Each week had a rhythm, a structure. I set myself goals, small achievements, titbits to keep me going and give a sense of time passing. My first goal each day was to get up and dressed. Mo would bring me breakfast in bed before he went to work and I would gradually come round, adjusting to the breathlessness induced by a change of posture. I would get up and have a bath, the shower at the top of the house being out of bounds because it involved climbing up another set of stairs with no chair-lift. Showers were tricky, anyway, because of the need to stand for a long time, and to move up and down to wash myself. But sometimes, as a treat, Mo would carry me up the stairs and keep watch in case I fainted in the shower. Baths were easier, although quite an effort to get in and out of, with many stops to gasp for breath. I would lie in the bath and peer down at my white chest and try and imagine what it would look like with a red scar down my sternum, think perhaps that this was the last time I would see it unmarked. I would daydream of all the things I could do with my new heart and lungs – run, walk up mountains, skip, dance, be able to stand on one leg, do the shopping. Go out without my entourage of helper, wheelchair, oxygen. Walk to the end of the road and post a letter.

Most days I would have visitors. My mother came round several times a week to help tidy up, iron, chat. She'd bring shopping, food, soup and kept my spirits up. Occasionally we would both have a little cry, but most of all we chatted, gossiped, she would tell me what her friends were up to, I would crack jokes and make her laugh. My father visited, drinking coffee and talking. Work colleagues kept me in touch with the gossip. Neighbours popped in, the children offering to help with errands, posting letters, taking back library books. My sisters visited and took me out for lunch, to cafes where we could park nearby and I could stagger in for an hour or so. Friends came round and seemed, between them, to have organised some kind of rota, arriving in a steady stream, not too many, never too few. Elaine took me out to visit garden centres, chatting about plans and planting, telling me of her travels. Sue, who had survived leukaemia, knew all about illness and I knew she knew what it was like to be so limited, to look death in the face. Cath arrived with stacks of mail-order catalogues, proclaiming: 'Just because you're dying doesn't mean you can't shop.'

Our neighbours Ann and Anthony decided that their contribution was to cook for us once a week, a welcome escape from the house and time-off cooking for Mo. My stubbornness meant I always walked over there, two doors away, refusing the wheelchair. However, the effect of food in my stomach, diverting even more oxygen away from my brain, made me sleepy and breathless and I invariably had to be carried home, either in a fireman's lift between Mo and Anthony, or on one occasion in a wheelbarrow.

I was touched by the effort people made for me but felt a bit guilty about it, as though I didn't deserve it. My brother Rob, travelling around Australia, had sent flowers, emails, words of encouragement. I'd emailed him to say that I was going on the transplant list. 'Christ,' came the reply from an internet café somewhere east of Perth. 'The lengths some people will go to draw attention to themselves.'

I knew he was joking, but part of me felt uncomfortable getting so much attention. I just wanted to be treated as normal, ignored, not having so many people be so *nice* to me. Sometimes people did not know what to say. After listening to my story, a story I was becoming increasingly bored with, they would, reluctantly at first, settle in to telling me their moans and stresses, invariably hesitating, stopping themselves in mid sentence to exclaim, 'Of course it is nothing compared to what you are going through.' I wondered whether being told that my problems were so much worse than anyone else's was supposed to make me feel better, or was some kind of misplaced empathy. I was happy to have a moan and groan to friends, knowing that it would be difficult for many of them to fully understand, but I was also still interested in other's lives, other's problems, gossip. I wanted to hear about the whole of human experience, not some sanitised version of it especially for invalids. I was always relieved when people could just be honest. 'You can't bloody die on me,' my friend Anna came out with one day, having worked through the usual 'how-are-you's and 'it'll be okay'. 'I really like you, you know. I don't really like just anyone. I'd really howl my eyes out at your funeral and make a right fool of myself. You can't put me through that.' I promised her I'd try not to, I'd try to behave. Some people tried to reassure me that things were going to work out and most of all I ignored it. How could anyone know? However, Jacky, my South African friend, warm as toast, huge-hearted, inspired me with her vision of what life could be, would be like for me. 'I just know you're going to be okay,' she said, over and over again. Somehow, from her, I believed it: maybe I was going to be okay.

Each day, I tried to do something to keep my mind off it all. I carried on writing a book on anxiety, my own fears simmering away but yet to erupt. I had Greek lessons, it being easier to worry about my lack of skill in conjugating irregular verbs and trying to remember vocabulary than think about what might lie ahead.

I never really had a chance to feel sorry for myself and I never did – it wasn't in my nature, somehow. Despite being so limited, my life being so small, I felt grateful for what I had. I was glad to have done so much when I could – travelled to Australia, New Zealand, Europe, Canada. Enjoyed my work, my friends and family. If this was it, then I felt I had lived the good life. Nothing to be ashamed of, not too much to regret. In 1993 I'd gone to see a careers advisor, who told me to make a list of things I wanted to do before I died. Some of them were wishful thinking, given my half a heart – run along a beach, be able to simultaneously walk upstairs and hold a conversation, go snorkelling in the Maldives. But many of them I'd attempted – for example, learning to dance. I'd had a go at ballroom dancing a few years previously. Despite having to do everything at half speed, stopping to gasp every few steps, I had an idea how to quick-step, waltz, cha-cha-cha. I could do a mean slow-motion rumba. In my life so far, I had lots to look back on. I wasn't lonely, depressed or in pain. I loved my husband. If this was it, then it wasn't so bad.

Time went on. Slowly, slowly, not always uncomfortably, but always with the sense of waiting. I played games with myself. I worked out that I would most likely get the call out of the blue, as a complete surprise, and so there was no point in thinking about it or planning it. Every time the little thought 'I wonder if it will be today' came into my mind, I figured that because I had had the thought and was therefore prepared, then it would definitely not be today so I could forget about it. I made sure I always had some good reason for not going to hospital in the next week – plans to see a friend, tickets for the theatre, a piece of writing to finish, a commitment to read a friend's dissertation. I upped the stakes, bought the most expensive tickets for Stratford in June, planned a holiday. The Queen's Jubilee came and went, with street parties and concerts. Friends came, I saw the world from waist height. Time passed.

7. The Call

8th–9th June 2002

ON SATURDAY 8TH JUNE I decided enough was enough. I was fed up with waiting. I would stop being so prepared. I emptied my hospital bag, put everything in the wash and realised having packed it in October it was now filled with heavier clothes than the warmth of June dictated. The Thursday before, we went to the open market and I bought some Vietnamese silk pyjamas. The stallholder enquired about my wheelchair and I told him, as I had told so many others, my story. He handed me his card saying I should come and see him in Vietnam next summer.

'That would be nice, but I may not be well enough then,' I replied.

'Of course you will be,' he said. 'You won't have to wait much longer now.'

Strange. Lots of people had passed on good wishes that I did not have to wait too much longer, but he seemed quite sure that the waiting was almost over. Maybe it was just a good sales-ploy – after all, I bought his pyjamas. But it left me with a shiver. That Saturday, I put his pyjamas in the pile to go back into the bag despite the fact that they were highly unsuitable for the rigours of hospital.

We settled down, as we did many weekends, to watch 'Casualty'. Five minutes before the end of the programme, the telephone rang. I would normally have left the answerphone to pick it up, not liking

69

to interrupt my favourite programmes, 'Casualty' and 'The Archers', but some instinct made me answer and I knew who it was before she spoke.

'Diana, it's Helen from Papworth. How are you?'

'I was fine until I heard your voice,' I quipped. This was no joke. 'No, I mean fine. Is this …?'

'Yes, we have a potential donor for you. Just a possibility at this stage, but we need you to come in.'

I was to be picked up in an hour.

Given all the things that have to be right when matching donor and recipient, transplants are a lottery. Or rather, nothing can be predicted with accuracy. Take most hospital waiting lists, for, say, a hip operation. If there are 200 people needing hip operations at one hospital, these people will be put on a list and steadily worked through. So, at any one time it is possible to say you have so many months, or years, to wait, before coming to the top of the list. With organ transplants, everyone is allocated according to how well they match with potential donors, not by rank on a list. Organs and recipients are matched on two main variables. Blood-group is the most important. If the donor's blood-type is incompatible with the recipient's, the organs will be immediately rejected. Being A positive, the second most common blood-group, was for me both good and bad news. Good in that having common group meant I had more donors in common. Bad in that there would be more people like me waiting. Another factor is to match donor and recipient according to size. This was, again, good news for me. Many of the people waiting for heart and lung transplants have cystic fibrosis and are often smaller in stature. Being tall meant I could match with a variety of donors, men and women. In addition to blood-group and size, some organ transplants such as kidneys are also matched on tissue-type antigens, called human leukocyte antigens, proteins linked to the immune response. While it is difficult to get a perfect HLA match, the nearer the better, or so the research shows.

While my blood-group and size increased my chances of having a transplant, the fact that I was, technically, still fairly well, would count against me. If two or more people are, by chance, an exact match for a set of organs, complex decisions have to be made based on clinical need. The person who is a medical emergency and likely to die the soonest without the transplant may well have priority over those who are stable. Since I was living at home rather than needing to be in hospital, able to have some quality of life and, as yet, had no other major medical problems, I was aware of being a low priority should a competitive situation arise. That night, luck was on my side and very clearly not on the side of my donor. I had got The Call.

The quality and urgency this time felt different from my false alarm the previous October. Somehow, this call meant business. I re-packed my bag, flinging clothes all over the place, trying to decide what to take, realising it was impossible since I could not, realistically, have any idea about what I would need. If I would need anything at all. In the end I packed two bags, one for immediate use, the other for the time when I was up and about again, should that be a possibility. The second contained shoes, the first, slippers. I put on my best turquoise underwear, like a maiden dressing for her wedding or a cadaver for the funeral. I just wanted to end this part of my life, whichever way it turned out, knowing that my knickers and bra matched. I put on jewellery Mo had given me, my rings, bracelets, gold and silver earrings and my great-aunt's pearl ring. In defiance of all the instructions not to bring valuables into hospital, I wanted to be surrounded by my symbols of love and endurance, the ring given to me by my mother, the bracelet marking my time with Mo. I wanted stuff normally saved for 'best' to accompany me on this particular journey.

We had agreed that we would not contact my parents or family until after the operation, since there was no point in anyone waiting and worrying unnecessarily. But there was one phone call I had to make.

'Jacky, it's me.' I was sitting on the loo, painting my toenails, to make the phone call.

'Di-Di? How are you?'

Jacky sounded mildly tipsy. I pictured her and her husband David sitting outside their cottage in Binsey, a tiny hamlet within Oxford, enjoying the warm evening, their two boys asleep at last. Julian, two and Gabriel, their four-year-old, who always called me Di-Di, had been concerned to hear that I was not well and had made me a big card saying 'I am sorry you are a bit sick. Please get better soon and come and have tea in the garden with us.'

'I'm fine, I think. I need to ask you a favour. Are you busy?' I asked her.

'Not very, we were just going to bed. What is it?'

'Can you go to the wishing-well and put some money in for me?' Up the road from Binsey is St Margaret's Church with a wishing-well. St Frideswide's well was a place of pilgrimage in medieval times and became Lewis Carroll's treacle-well in *Alice in Wonderland.* Jacky solved many problems with the help of a few coins thrown, with a wish, into its muddy depths. Tonight I could definitely do with a bit of divine intervention. 'I've got the call,' I went on. 'I'm going up to Papworth now. It may be nothing, but it may mean …'

'Oh, Di-Di,' she said.

'Lots of money. About a thousand pounds. I'm sure a cheque will do.' A feeble joke to stop my voice trembling.

'I'll go now. I'll get my bike. We're holding thumbs for you. Good luck and lots and lots of love.' I could hear her voice trembling now. We would both start crying if the conversation went on and I couldn't face that at the moment. We said goodbye, sent hugs down the phone. I wondered if I'd ever see her again.

After the allocated hour, the doorbell rang. The vehicle had arrived, my carrier to the next world. It should really have been a coach-and-four flying its ghostly voyage through the night. Instead it was a maroon people-carrier with hard upright seats and a solemn driver. Mo came with me this time, sitting next to me holding my hand. It was not quite dark when we left, and we shot through the streets out of Oxford, on to the big roundabout before the motorway and off, overtaking and overtaking. I felt mildly sick, trying not to get my hopes up, but hoping too that this would be another abortive journey, since the alternative seemed too big to contemplate. If I thought it was real this time, would my thoughts increase or decrease the likelihood of it being real? If I said to myself it was a false alarm, would my thoughts have some mythical power to change history, to bring the donor back to life, or make his or her organs unsuitable for me? Someone has died, I kept thinking, someone has died. We carried on up the M40, on to the M25, miraculously clear and on to the A1. The driver was getting messages on his radio at regular intervals, asking him where he was, telling him to speed up. 'We've moved from a blue light to a red light,' he told us. 'That means we are priority.' We began to approach familiar stretches of road. The driver, rather than speeding up, seemed to slow down, and the last few miles were agonisingly slow. I have always found that the last part of any journey is the worst: the long car-journeys back from Devon as a child were endless once we hit the outskirts of Oxford, the time dragging even more when the destination was in sight. We passed signs to Papworth and the last mile seemed to take a decade.

At the hospital, I was wheeled up to an empty six-bedded side-ward. Bright lights, white sheets on the beds. A fish-tank, surprisingly bright and colourful. Patterned curtains. I made one of the beds my base and settled down. It was the middle of the night and I wanted to go to sleep. I wanted to be in my bed at home, reading before putting out the night, feeling Mo by my side and the cats at our feet. Comfort, familiarity. At midnight I was sitting on a hard, iron-framed bed, awaiting my fate. Helen came to talk, explain what would happen. I would see the doctor to check everything was fine, take blood-samples, then wait to see whether we could go ahead.

'And can we?' I asked.

'It all looks good at the moment, but as you know, things can change,' Helen replied with her usual combination of cheerful optimism and caution. 'But, yes, at the moment we are going ahead.'

Going ahead.

The doctor, Kumud, white coat, smiling, took my history again. Checked for any current problems, infections, chest problems, breathing difficulties. My turquoise bra seemed incongruous in the ward, but I needed it there to keep my identity – I am not just a patient, I wanted to say, a piece of flesh to be operated on, but a personality, a woman, the sort of person who does not always abide by the rules, do what she is told.

I did everything I was told. I gave my blood, my history, my consent. I signed a form giving my body over to the hands of men and women in masks, consenting to the transplant and, if necessary, a post-mortem if the surgery was not successful. I sat patiently on the bed with Mo, waiting. People in and out, giving news. Yes, it is still going ahead so far. I had heard from others that the operation could be cancelled right up to the last minute. One potential transplantee I had spoken to on the telephone, Michael, said that he had got to the point of having his chest shaved ready for surgery when he was suddenly sent home, disappointed. So my hopes and fears were hovering but not definite. But when the driver, who would have taken us home had the transplant not gone ahead, was sent home himself, I thought they must mean business.

At 2.10 am, Helen came back to the ward with a wheelchair to take me to theatre. By this time, I was dressed in a pale blue hospital gown, a ridiculous garment that ties down the back leaving a large, undignified gap. My underwear, jewellery, wedding-rings, make-up and nail-varnish had all been taken off. I went, scrubbed clean and naked, to my fate. I was wheeled through to intensive care to be shown an empty bed which was to be mine after the operation. Intensive care looked similar to an ordinary ward, only with more monitors and drips surrounding the beds. One woman, a breathing tube coming from her mouth, lay in her bed, apparently sleeping peacefully. The lights were dim, the atmosphere calm. I thought I would probably be all right here.

On to theatre. A small anaesthetic room outside the main operating-theatre, a narrow metal bed for me to lie on, trying to hold together the flapping back of my gown. The room was crammed with people wearing masks, blue hats, gowns, unrecognisable, busy, not paying me much attention. I realised, really realised, at this point what was happening.

'Does this mean it is going ahead?' I asked.

Helen laughed. 'Yes, we wouldn't do this to you if it wasn't.'

'Oh, can I go home now please?'

The anaesthetist holding my hand, ready to insert a large needle, paused and looked at me.

'You can if you want. It is your choice. We can all go home if you like.'

The full weight of responsibility on my shoulders. I'd given my consent, but for a moment was not sure. If it went wrong, if I was not to survive, it would be up to me. This was my choice, my very own choice, nobody else's. Despite doing as much as possible in my life, living at the edge of my limits, there were some risks I would never take. I always wore a seat belt, kept to the speed limit, practised safe sex, avoided walking alone at night, carried a mobile phone, made safe investments. Flossed my teeth. Wore wellington boots when changing a light-bulb. Yet here was I taking the biggest risk of all with my life. If ten of these operations were starting at the same time, the probability game dictated that one or two people would not come out alive.

'OK, I'm ready.' I lay down on the hard surface, feeling the cold against my exposed bum. My wrist was hurting, as the anaesthetist searched for an artery with a long, thick needle. I looked at Mo, standing by and smiled. 'I'll see you later…'

*   *   *

Voices are asking me to say my name. I try to speak but nothing comes out. I try again. They keep on asking me questions. Voices, voices. I wave my hand, wanting to write something down. A pen is put into my hand, paper. I try to write. Nothing will come out. I have no words. I can't breathe I can't breathe I can't talk I can't breathe I can't.

*   *   *

They are speaking Greek, two young women at the end of the bed. Greek. I know Greek.

Μιλάω Ελληνικά. I can speak Greek, I tell them.

Τι; What?

Εγώ μιλάω Ελληνικά.

The voices are laughing at me. Is it my accent? They are discussing one of the doctors. I want to chime in, tell them I think he's rather good-looking.

Όμορφος είναι; Νομίζω ότι είναι όμορφος.

*   *   *

I'm lying, floating in the middle of a room, beds all around me, but far away. Lights, voices. I don't know where I am, what has happened, but I am too tired to care. There are two of them, one fair, one dark, pulling me up into a sitting position, telling me to swing my legs round off the bed. I am floppy, rag-doll-like. Nauseous, the room spinning. I have to move towards a chair, a large brown leather hospital chair next to the bed, across the other side of the universe. I have to take two steps, I stagger and the chair slides across one of the tubes coming out of my chest. I feel terrible pain in my chest. It is hard to breathe. I cry out in distress, no please no something is wrong please help me. I am moved back towards the bed, moved back to sit, comfort, support. Mo is there, looking at the tube. It is leaking air, he says. Is this right? It is all confused, confusing. Something is wrong but I do not know what and what to do, what can I do. What a state. Someone else is looking at the tube, discussing it. Something is wrong with the equipment. It must have been sabotaged, someone is trying to kill me. My chest hurts, I cannot breathe. Sudden tugging, suction at my chest and slowly the pain goes down.

'We've put you on suction. It's all right. One of your lungs is leaking air.' A disembodied voice. I am not reassured. I'm going to die, this is it, they are killing me. A blond doctor is talking at me, nonsense. I want him to go away, take notice of what I am saying.

'You arrogant little sod.' Whose voice? Mine.

*　　　　*　　　　*

It is the middle of the night. The kindness of the Greeks is bestowed upon me. Katerina, my very own dedicated nurse, the kindest soul on earth, is washing me. Washing away all the yellow paint over my chest, washing away my fear and pain. The cloth is abrasive, exfoliating, rubbing it all away. I want her to stay for ever. She is rolling me over, washing my back, heaven, my legs. My bum. That is private. No one has ever washed me there before. Except as a baby. I am a baby, therefore.

*　　　　*　　　　*

I am sick. Sick. Sick. Thirsty, thirsty, thirsty. Someone is telling me I cannot drink, am not allowed too much water. Ice cubes in my mouth, sucking greedily. Another, another. Then ice-lollies, coke-flavoured, orange. Voices discussing, 'Ice is allowed, a drop of fluid, just a drop.' I want pints. What is happening?

8. Mind over Matter

12th–13th June 2002

I AM SITTING UP. It is daytime. I am offered tea, breakfast. It must be Sunday morning. Last night was Saturday, I remember. Saturday night, late, I came here. I must have had the operation but I can't remember. I am not in the same place I have been all night, but it is the same place feeling all different. I am surrounded by tubes, some coming out of my body. Machines, bleeping, flashing. A nurse tells me she will take out my catheter. Ohmygod, ohmygod, no one can touch me down there. That is private. It is going to be hell, agony.

'Have you done this before?' I ask. She finds this amusing. I am not joking. I need to know.

'No, no this is my first time. You can tell me what to do.' I join in the joke but inside, shake. I have to do this. The first of many occasions, thousands, millions of episodes of being brave.

It does not hurt at all, I did not even notice it. She pulls at a rubber tube disappearing between my legs, which expands as it comes out.

'There, all done. You can wee on your own now.'

Another nurse, who I am told is a trainee under supervision, brings me my breakfast. Tea, rice krispies made with hot milk. I look and burst into tears.

'I don't want hot milk. Cold milk. You can't have bloody rice krispies with hot milk!' I am indignant, outraged. The joking nurse whips them away, tells off the trainee, who produces, shamefaced,

78

another bowl. I am ashamed of myself. It's all right, thank you. I should not have made a fuss. I must be a better patient.

I look at my feet. They are pink. Pale pink nails. My finger tips too, pink. Not blue. Pink.

A crowd of white-coated doctors fly in through the door and swoop down as one to land at the side of my bed. The flock-leader is Mr Large, the surgeon who performed my operation. He beams at me, takes my hand. 'Well done. The operation was a complete success. A textbook case.' He turns to his flock who caw and chirp amongst themselves. I love him and all of them. They are my gods and goddesses. My saviours.

Mr Large is telling me things, giving me information, lots of words like a jumble. I watch a speech bubble come from his mouth but none of the words mean anything. 'Do you have any questions?' he asks.

Umm. What to ask. It must be good, my first question of God. Am I a worthy human being? Am I going to live? How long for? Can I go home now?

'Um, who was my donor?' I watch the words come out of my mouth. Where did that come from? Mr Large reassures me, shaking his head, ready to swoop off to the next bed. 'You don't need to worry about that. You are much better off now we've taken all that mess out of you. You must look forward now, concentrate on getting better.' I thank him and smile. He and the flock are off.

It is all action. Drips are changed, dressings checked, faces washed. Notes are read, charts drawn up, plans made. I am to be transferred to the ward at 11 am.

'That was quick,' I say. 'I thought I would be here for a few days,' I say to the nurse.

'You have been,' she tells me. 'Today is Tuesday. You came here early Sunday morning. So you've been here two days already.'

How can it manage to be Tuesday? I have no sense of time passing. Only a few fragments of dreams. I move with the help of Mo and two nurses, into a wheelchair, accompanied by pumps, drips and a bottle into which flows the output from the drains, sucking blood and fluids from my chest. I am wheeled miles, about 200 yards, down the corridor into Mallard Ward, the main surgical ward, into a bright four bedded room. I am the only occupant so can choose my bed. I go for the one next to the big window. I cannot see very well, am not sure if I have my glasses on, but think I can see trees. They will be nice to look at. I am installed in the bed along with drips, wires, drains, pumps. I am plugged into a vacuum-cleaner on the wall to suck out air and debris from my chest. The nurse puts an oxygen mask on me and, crossly, I take it off, wanting to scream 'The whole point of this is that I don't have to bloody use bloody oxygen.' I can't string the words together, but she seems to understand and replaces the mask with a nasal cannula. 'Only for a day or so,' she says. I collapse in the bed, try without success to get comfortable and Mo sits in the chair. Everyone leaves and we are left alone.

After the bright lights of intensive care, its busyness, one-to-one nursing, reassurance, help, support, we are now on our own. I am on my own. We wait. What am I supposed to be doing with myself? I am overwhelmed and feel awful. Too awful to feel anything much, just terrible. A nursing auxiliary comes round and asks me if I want any lunch. Lunch? What is that? I realise, for the first of what is to be many times, that I am feeling sick. But I know I must eat. I ask for toast. I go through the motions of chewing a bit then a bit more. A pretty nurse from the Philippines comes to talk to me, to go through my details.

'What is your religion?' she asks. I've never been too clear on that one, but if I ever wanted to hedge my bets, it was now.

'I was a Christian and right now I need a bit of help,' I say to her in a tiny voice. 'I'm Anglican. Church of England. I've been confirmed. I used to go to church a lot when I was a teenager, but it was mainly to meet boys. But I did pray. And I promise I will go to church more, pray more now.'

'That's fine,' she says, ticking the C of E box. My next of kin? My God, do they think they need that information, that emergency information?

'Mo,' I say, 'or my parents, but please do not disturb them, they will be so worried and I don't want to worry my mum especially. What about them, do they know?' Somehow, with me talking gibberish, we get through the form. She goes away. We wait.

Mo has been contacting everyone to tell them I've had the operation. My parents. My mother answered the phone early on Sunday morning. They had friends to stay that weekend and would have been busy entertaining, cooking, making coffee, being hospitable. I know they will be tired already without this on top. I picture her in her dressing-gown standing by the phone in the hall, hearing the news, tears coming into her eyes, speechless, wanting to break down and weep.

'I told them you are doing fine, they are pleased, I'll phone them later,' he tells me. The Sanders-Exchange would have done its work, the news spreading around the rest of the family: my two sisters, my brother in Australia. Has anyone contacted Rob? No, his mobile phone is not working, he's in the middle of a desert somewhere. My friends, Jacky, Anna, Cath, Sue, Elaine, Amanda, the key people involved in the process, will be hearing it. I feel like royalty and in receipt of a wave of good wishes. I know they will be sending out hope to me. Mo looks exhausted. I feel guilty: am I doing this to everyone, I wonder?

I realise that I have very little voice. I want to say things but I can't. I can hardly speak. It is hard to breathe, my chest feels extraordinary, indescribable, as though I am enclosed by a tight barbed-wire corset with wires extending into my throat. My whole body aches and I feel sick. Not like food poisoning, but as though every cell, every molecule is sick. I start retching, vomiting. Someone comes and brings me what looks like a bowler hat made of compressed, grey paper. Another nurse comes, carrying a pot of pills, the first of a lifetime of pots of pills. There are at least twelve and I have to take them.

'But I feel so sick. What can I do?' I ask. I remember that I am on a surgical ward, where many people must get sickness following anaesthesia. The nurses must be experts, have tips and hints up their sleeves to help us. They will get me through. I will learn what to do.

The nurse looks at me coolly, slightly shrugs her shoulders. 'Mind over matter, I would think,' she says.

I am, momentarily, too stunned to feel sick. Is that it? Is it really so easy? As I watch her blurred figure receding away from the bed, feeling, no doubt, that she has scored a victory over surgical patients who dare, dare to confess to feeling sick, I lean over the bowler hat and vomit energetically. Mind: zero. Matter: one.

*   *   *

Mo has gone to the canteen to make more telephone calls. A figure is standing at the end of the bed, looking at me, head tilted to one side. Smiling. Tall, lanky, wearing a suit a size too large. A boy, no more than twelve or thirteen, heading through a growth spurt.

'Why aren't you at school?' I whisper to him.

'G'day.' Bass voice, must have broken early. 'I'm Peter. How are you feeling?'

'Who are you? I don't remember you?'

'Peter Hopkins, your consultant. I've been looking after you.' Australian drawl, pleasant, soothing.

'Why do I feel so awful? I can't breathe properly. You must have sewn up my diaphragm. Something is wrong,' I plead. Someone to help, someone to take it all away.

'You're doing just fine. Fine. No problems at all. We're really pleased.' He squeezes my toes.

'I'm feeling terribly sick. I can't keep anything down. I can't control it, really, I am trying.'

'That's fine, we'll give you something.' He's gone. Shortly followed by a nurse bearing a syringe. He starts fiddling with something on my neck. What is that, I ask. 'We've put in a line in your neck veins, for intravenous drugs. This is cyclizine, it will help the sickness,' he explains. Something cool is moving through my neck. Immediately, miraculously, the nausea vanishes. I feel the tide recede, something of myself return. Relief. I can eat, take the medication, be a good patient.

The day progresses. The other beds in the ward have filled up, patients moved from intensive care or other wards. I cannot see them properly, but reply in a whisper to their greetings. It is never quiet, always something going on, always people around. I am visited by nurses, injecting things through the mass of tubing in my neck; nursing assistants, distinguishable by their pink uniforms, bringing tea, water, meals, chat, kindness, smiles. Peter comes back with other people, who stand at the end of the bed and talk. I cannot make out faces, so am not sure whether these are new people or those I've seen before. Helen comes, smiling, pleased. It all went so well, she tells me, despite my protestations of feeling awful. The physiotherapist comes, shows me how to sit up in bed.

'You must not put any weight on your arms,' she tells me. 'You need to protect your sternum, otherwise it may come open.' An image of my centre ripping open, new organs spilling out onto the bed. 'No, I won't let that happen,' I promise her. She ties a blue rope to the end of the bed, which I have to pull on to lift myself up.

'Use your stomach muscles and pull gently on your arms.' What stomach muscles? I try and remain stationary. I pull on my arms and nothing happens. She puts a hand into the small of my back and gently pushes. I rock up. Easy, I can do that.

She tells me I have to breathe deeply, cough. She gives me a rolled up towel to hold against my sternum to protect it. I try and cough and nothing comes out but a squeak. They've taken my cough away. I squeak with distress.

'It's okay, it's just because of the ventilation tube,' she reassures me. 'You can get a bit of irritation, it'll settle down in a few days.' She explains that the nerves to the lungs have been cut so I no longer have nerve connections between my lungs and the rest of the body. Normally, the presence of anything other than air in the lungs triggers a cough reflex to get rid of any intruders, but after a transplant there is no cough-message and so, no automatic cough. I therefore have to cough to order, regularly, to keep my lungs clear.

We keep going, together breathing in and coughing, until something comes up. I spit obligingly into a pot and she looks delighted.

'You need to keep doing that,' she urges me, 'to clear your lungs, get them working.'

I sit on the edge of the bed and breathe deeply, then cough, breathe deeply, cough, until I begin to get the idea of what a cough is like.

Somehow we get through to the end of the day. I have managed to take several pots of pills, having no idea what they all are – the nurses tell me their names, what they are for and I quickly forget. There is a hole in my brain, everything leaks out. Jumbled, confused. I manage to eat soup, keep it down. Toast, too. I drink, milk, water, strong tea. I talk to Mo, hear about where he is staying, a room in the village. I manage to pee, too, much to my and the nurses' relief. I've been told that peeing could be a problem after having been catheterised, which would mean another catheter would have to be inserted. More invasion. Anxiously, I sit on the commode, tell my bladder it has to behave and after a long wait, relief at last.

It is time for Mo to go. I lie awake throughout the night. I seem to be in a different place now, moved to a different location, floating through space. Sleep does not come, but for a moment, I am standing on the top of a square building looking out across a flat landscape to a flat horizon and sea. It is grey, desolate. I am shouting 'Don't fence me in.' Only for a moment, then I am back in the ward. I ring the bell. A young male nurse comes and talks to me, holds my hand, soft words, sympathy. 'It's difficult, but you're doing fine,' he says. 'You must try and rest now.' His voice is soothing, kind. He murmurs to me in the darkness, then goes.

I long for ordinariness, the feeling of neutral comfort in my body, the familiarity of my own bed, mattress, duvet. The ordinariness of the bedroom, the taste of my usual tea, the cats jumping up to greet me. Stroking, purring. The ordinariness of the view from the bedroom window, the backs of neighbours' houses and the trees, the sound of the telephone and traffic going by. The ordinariness of the routine of my days. It is all gone. My body is alien, troublesome, deeply uncomfortable. What could possibly have prepared me for feeling so awful? I thought, by forty-six, that I had collected enough of a variety of life-experiences, pain, illness, sadness, divorce, a broken foot, bereavements, that awfulness would become somehow familiar. But lying here, trying to sleep, my bum squashing into the rubber mattress, pillows falling off, unable to see much beyond the curtain at the end of the bed, I realise that this is something new.

I do not even have words or images or memories to describe how I feel. Terrible, toxic, tight, unable to breathe – the closest is to say I feel poisoned. Every cell in my body feels strange. The sensations from my skin are all wrong. My breathing is different, extraordinary, like someone has sewn up my diaphragm and I am breathing against a great weight. My head has been shaken and twisted and put back on the wrong way round so that thoughts and words come out backwards. My body is in constant motion, trembling deep inside, agitation – terrible agitation, inside and outside. My brain is whirring without going anywhere. My hands shake so I cannot hold a glass of water. I feel sick in a way I've never felt sick before, nausea that is not nausea in itself, it is me – I am nausea. I remember that no one I've spoken to about having a transplant said it was painful. Painful I could do. Pain is familiar, pain is painful, unbearable at times, the sort of feeling that makes you want to run, escape, move, reach out for painkillers. I expected that pain would be my first sensation. But not painful. I am deeply, profoundly uncomfortable.

It is still nighttime. I have an impression of darkness outside, subdued lighting in the ward, rattles of trolleys, voices, footsteps in the corridor but no one near me. I want to talk to my parents but it is the middle of the night and there's no phone. I reach out for my notebook I've put by the side of the bed and try to write them a letter. 'I'm okay, don't worry about me,' I write in a shaky hand. 'I can't talk, never have I been so quiet.' I manage to write a few words before the notebook slides on to the floor. For the first time in many years, I say my prayers. I wriggle myself into a straight position and try and supplicate my hands together on my chest without knocking the tubes out. I wonder if God minds if my hands are not quite in the right place for proper prayers. I pray for my donor. However bad I am feeling, however ill, frightened, angry, somewhere else a lot more people are suffering far more. I pray for the family, the husband or wife, mother, father, siblings, children, friends. A lot of people to pray for and I do not know any of them. I imagine pushing my prayers out into the air to travel to wherever they should be. I don't know which God I am praying to, but it doesn't matter. Any will do just now. I pray for my body to recover, to get over this, to heal. And I pray for Mo to be able to cope. I know I have a long way to go, a long time of feeling bad. There's no easy way out. I have to do this, one moment, one tiny moment at a time.

9. Incarceration

13th–23rd June 2004

ONLY MUCH LATER AM I able to watch television programmes about hospitals, visit friends in hospital, without feeling traumatised. Those early days in Papworth I simply did not know what to do with myself. It was as though all my resources had been stripped away, all sense of being able to manage had been cut out with my organs. I was unable to gain any perspective, to see that my state was temporary, that all things would pass. Cardiac surgery has been described by Oxford surgeon Stephen Westaby as a 'controlled road-traffic accident'. I'd been knocked to pieces, pulled out alive, kept from dying by machines, drugs and stitches, and had remained conscious to feel it all. I wished at times I had not survived. But I had. And I had to get on with it.

*   *   *

The next morning comes. Mo returns, hollow-eyed. I weep. 'Please take me home,' I beg him. I get out of bed and stand to hug him, careful of my chest-drains and tubes coming out of my neck and arms. I am homesick, I want to see the cats, I want my bed. I am a hungry child, unable to contain the bad feelings; I'm a needy, desperate baby. I realise what is wrong. When they took out my heart, they took out my fighting spirit. The bit of me that could cope with anything, the fighter, the stubborn, sod-the-world-I'll-show-them, I-can-do-this-even-if-everyone-else-says-I-cannot, the just-stay-calm, stay-with-it, use-your-inner-resources Diana had disappeared. Off in the pathology lab with all my unwanted parts.

'Put them back!' I whisper, 'I want my heart back. My lungs, my poor lungs, I want them back. Please, please.' I never expected to feel this. My heart and lungs which had given me so much trouble, which were incompetent, which could not get me dressed in the morning or hold a conversation, they are gone for ever. I am overwhelmed with grief, raw sorrow, loss. Please put them back. I remember all the things we did together. A memory of myself, age twenty-three or so, climbing up the Pentland Hills south of Edinburgh. A cold, windy day. I struggle up slowly, stopping for breath, seeing the top of the hill further away as I climb. We make it to the top, my holey heart racing, my overworked lungs struggling to produce a paltry supply of oxygen, and breathe in the Scottish air, preparing for the long walk down. And we climbed up mountains together in New Zealand, I and my heart and lungs and my walking companion, an eighty-year-old arthritic friend who was a good match for my slow, breathless pace. My heart and lungs went ballroom dancing with me, gasping, exhilarated by the steps, the music. We coped and managed and got by, despite the odds. And here I was, rejecting my lifelong companions, part of me, throwing them away, discarding them, all to feel so terrible. How could I have done such a thing? I longed for the ordinariness of my loud, erratic heartbeat, the familiar gasping sensations.

Time expands, contracts into an awareness of seconds passing, then expands. Just like when I was a child, the time between now – ten to eleven in the morning – and lunchtime at twelve seems to stretch to infinity. How can I get through it? I reach for Mo's hand. He is asleep on the chair, hand limp but still outstretched to mine. How can he sleep? What is sleep anyway? Will I ever be able to sleep again? I remember what Mo said – a minute at a time. So that is seventy minutes to go, and one has gone in working that out. Sixty-nine minutes. A lifetime. My eyes still can see no further than a few feet. Outside the window I get a sense of a sunny day – sky flits in and out between the blur of the branches, but when I look again it recedes into a short-sighted aura. They've taken my eyesight away. Sarah, a nurse whom I come to rely on for comfort, words of wisdom, strength to get through, appears at the end of the bed.

'I have to give you your medication,' she says.

'I can't see properly, I can't focus – what is it? What's wrong?' I ask her. Sarah sits on the bed, closer, so I can see her. Brown hair, plump-pretty, brown eyes. A kind face.

'Oh, it's very common.' she explains. 'Lots of people find it difficult to see after heart surgery. It is the effect of the bypass machine. The machine compresses your red blood cells, it affects your vision for a while.'

'What, years or something?' I ask, suddenly anxious. I've lost my heart and lungs and now my vision.

'No, no, just a week to ten days. It will come back.'

Tears of relief. It is normal. Expected. Other people have it, spending time in a miasma of short-sightedness and then recovering. If it is such a common thing, why could I not have been warned, or given this information at an earlier stage? Ten days. I calculate. Today is Wednesday, the operation was Sunday, so I should be fine by next Tuesday. But that is years away, years, yet more time to be got through, like forging a path through treacle, wading through mud. I look at my watch. It is now ten past eleven. Twenty whole minutes have passed and one problem has been solved. There, it is possible to do this.

*   *   *

I am a powerless, helpless patient. I receive the drugs into my system, take the medication, fill myself with anti-emetics to stop my body doing what it desperately wants to do, eject the poisons. I accept the poisons necessary to my survival and try and make sense of it all. I do as I am told, sit on the bed and breathe deeply, cough, move my legs. Move between the bed and the chair, shrug my shoulders, wiggle my feet. I eat what I can manage, sit and wait. I try and sleep, catching moments at a time, when I lie cocooned in a white, cellular hospital blanket on my bed, slipping into a state that is not sleep, but when time seems to pass faster. I snore, Mo tells me, indicating that I have slept, but it does not feel like it.

Figures appear at the end of the bed, doctors sweeping in, white-coated, to beam at me, review my drug chart, confer, cross out medications, add new ones, listen to my chest, then swoop off again to the next bed. Kumud, the doctor I saw just before the operation, comes to see me regularly, sits on the bed, smiling, chatting, encouraging. He tells me to 'relax, take it easy.' 'How can I relax like this?' I answer him, ready for an argument. 'How would you like it, being cut open and trussed up like a chicken, not being able to do anything?' He laughs. 'I'd hate it,' he agrees. I learn only later that he was the surgeon who had put in my new heart and lungs, sewn me up afterwards. I spent a lot of time talking to someone who'd had my heart in his hands.

Nurses come to do my observations, take my blood pressure, measure the oxygen saturation of my blood. The first time this was done, I whooped with pleasure. 100 per cent. My blood, starved of oxygen for the first forty-six years of my life, carrying no more than 70 per cent, 75 on a good day, was now 100 per cent. I had passed the first test of normality. I loved seeing it. When the machine measured only 98 or 99 per cent, I learned to breathe deeply with my new lungs and boost it up to 100. Just as when a baby is congratulated for deep burps after feeding, my 100 per cent reading is met with murmurs of approval all round. In fact I am in excellent shape.

Excellent shape but feeling like death. I snatch my first looks at my chest. A large, bruised scar running down my sternum ending just above my belly. No signs of stitches, which are all internal, but two ends of what looks like fishing-line come out from the top and bottom of the scar fastened by white plastic beads. If I knock these beads off, will I unravel? Then the most revolting of all, four plastic tubes emerge from wounds in my belly, tubes about two centimetres in diameter, with bloody liquid filtering through them. They lead into a large plastic jar containing blood-filled water, from which emerges another tube attached to a suction pump at the wall. Air and liquid are being vacuumed from my chest.

Kumud tells me that there is a hole in one of my lungs, a small tear which is leaking air. If the air was not pumped out, it would build up in my chest cavity causing the lungs to collapse. This was what happened in intensive care, the lung rupturing causing painful pressure in my chest. The tear will take a few days to mend, he says, but it is common and nothing to worry about. As well as the main scar and chest drains, wires emerge from each side of my chest – the pacing wires, which can be attached to a pacing machine if the heart beat becomes irregular. From my neck, a large tube connected to a mass of smaller tubes, sealed with red, white and blue plastic valves. From my arm, another line attached to the blue pump. Frankenstein.

Movement is not easy, but I am assured that none of the tubes can come loose. The physiotherapist visits again and shows me other exercises for my legs and arms to keep things moving. I have something to do, to work at. I gradually gain confidence in shifting from the bed to the chair and back again. I shrug my shoulders, twist and turn, lift my arms and remind my body it is designed for action. I stand by the bed, raising and lowering myself on tiptoe; I swing my leg up and down, in and out, to remind myself I have leg muscles. Over the next few days I start walking on the spot, walking, marching, faster and faster to try and get out of breath. I am brought an exercise bike, stationed at the end of the bed and I climb aboard with my drains still tethered to the wall and start pedalling. I imagine myself cycling out of the ward, flying down the corridors, shooting out of the hospital, cycling across fields, down roads, along rivers, beaches. Pedalling along with the wind in my face. My fellow bed mate lends me her Beach Boys tape and I pedal through 'Good vibrations and 'I get around'. My muscles scream and ache, my wound objects, I feel warm but not breathless. No sudden exhaustion, no blueness, no gasping.

My bowels become a major problem. Firstly from lack of activity,

I swell up as though seven months pregnant. The nurses come to give me heparin injections into my bloated belly and I wonder, as the needle goes in, whether I will pop. I take thick yellow medicine to move things along, without success. Then suppositories, which do the trick within the hour. Next, three days of acute diarrhoea. None of which would have been a great problem if I could get to the bathroom, but instead I am confined to a commode. Whoever designed the commode never tried it. I do not get used to not being able to wash properly and it is several long days before one of the nurses has the brilliant idea of adding another couple of feet to my suction tube so I can reach the basin in the ward.

Days pass and sleepless nights. I am a zombie from lack of sleep. The nausea and sickness are overtaken by unmanageable anxiety and shaking, a terrified, raw fear of everyone and everything. My thoughts constantly turn to what might go wrong. My tubes might come flying out and my lungs collapse. Someone might trip over the machinery, come landing on me and split my chest open. I might catch some terrible infection, a slow, lingering death. I will never get home. I will never be able to run. What if it all went wrong at this late stage? I am only all right when Mo, my saviour and strength, is around. Everyone else is out to harm me, they are incompetent, they may make a mistake. I am out of control. I shake and worry, worry and shake, what if, what if, what if all day and night. The nurses ask me to rate my anxiety level several times a day and record it on my folder, tell me it is normal, it will pass. They reassure me, answer my questions, explain, soothe, make it better. Kindness, professionalism, knowledge – I am moved to tears by what they are offering me.

One week after the operation, I have a fibreoptic bronchoscopy where a tube is inserted down my windpipe into my lungs to clear any secretions and to look at how the sutures are healing. I am told about this three days beforehand to give me plenty of time to worry myself into a state of nervous apprehension. More surgery. More anaesthetics. More things for me to be unable to remember afterwards.

And, most significantly, more opportunities for things to go wrong, mistakes to be made. When Monday arrives, I am ready to jump out of my skin at the slightest thing. I am allowed a cup of tea and one piece of toast at 6.30 am after another sleepless night, then I wait. The nurses all seem quite relaxed. I watch carefully for signs of deep sympathy, embarrassed glances or hushed tones when the night nurses inform the morning shift of my plans for today – 'Diana's going for a bronchoscopy at noon.' There is nothing I can detect, but no doubt they are good actors. Shortly before noon I say my last farewells to Mo, ready to go to my fate. We arrive at the X-ray suite and I go into a small cubicle to put on a backless gown. In the biopsy room I sit and wait while the doctor and radiologist fiddle with the machinery. It looks faulty to me. I rack my brains for information about the success or failure rate of biopsies. I cannot remember any episodes of 'Casualty' featuring extreme trauma caused by bronchoscopy failure in post-transplant patients, but there is always a first time. I look round the room – large machines, several monitors and various boxes on shelves above the machinery. I see what will happen. The boxes are going to fall off onto the machines, the shock of which would cause the doctor to jump, causing terrible damage to my lungs.

'For God's sake, get a grip, woman.'

My inner voice is so loud it could have come from the walls. Here was I, a psychologist with years of experience of treating people with anxiety problems, writing a book on anxiety, working myself into a lather of fear and trepidation over something which was routine and most probably entirely safe. I've been scanning for danger, allowing thoughts and stories to magnify in my already knackered brain. I laugh at myself and try to focus my attention on something else. I start talking to the nurse, asking her when her shift ends, what she was going to do that evening, what is on television. My anxiety begins to decrease. We get going. I lie on the bed, an oxygen tube is put in one nostril, I have a sensation of something else being pushed down my nose, two women leaning towards me. Vague, jumbled sensations. I am being lifted up to sitting.

'It's all over now. Well done. Everything looked fine.' A woman's voice.

'Is it over? That's it? I'm still alive?'

'Of course you are. We do try not to kill people, you know.' The doctor sounds affronted, but then smiles when she sees my face, furrowed with anxiety. 'It's fine, it's very routine. You'll probably have to have lots more of these,' she explains. For some reason, I feel reassured. Reassured that I have survived, got over one more milestone. I am taken back to the ward and lie in my bed, feeling hungry. Hungry. The first time since the operation, those familiar, welcome sensations. And calmer. I ask for toast, ice-cream. The anxiety seems to have receded. The world is benign. I am safe once more.

Over the next year-long few days, I am processed through a refined and organised system. Each morning at six the tea-trolley arrives. I have not slept, or if so, only for minutes at a time and have lain in bed, listening to the ducks waking up on the pond outside the window, the birds beginning their chorus. I've listened to several readings of the news on the radio, listened to my neighbours stir, grunt, mutter, snore, get up to pad to the bathroom. The arrival of the trolley heralds relief, entering back into the normality of the day after the demons of the night. We sit up, muttering and groaning to get comfortable, decide how many sugars we want this morning, stir and sip. We start chatting, voices across the room. 'How did you sleep? How are you this morning? What's the craic for today?' By now, we are a gang, a family, the four ladies in side-room C. Lisa, who has cheated death by emergency surgery to remove clots from her heart, spent her twenty-first birthday in a coma and had to cancel her wedding. After long days of delirium she awoke, cheerful, optimistic. Ann, who had a heart transplant a week before mine, is doing well. She tells me about a terrible time in intensive care, when she had several fits which had affected her badly and she was initially very angry about having had the operation at all. 'But I'm fine now,' she says. 'I'm glad I had the transplant. I'd never have been able to walk by myself as far as the bathroom without it.' She is showing me how it can be in a week's time. She is able to go to the bathroom and each afternoon, goes to the gym. I am jealous. And my neighbour, Irene, who has had a valve replaced, needs a pacemaker, can also go to the bathroom. We chat, compare notes on our doctors, discuss our families, commiserate our setbacks and celebrate our successes. The first bowel movement after days of constipation. Telephone calls from distant friends. Good results from tests. We help each other make the time pass, share crosswords, moans.

After the tea-trolley comes the handover, when the nurses congregate at the end of each bed to discuss the night's events and plans for the day. I glow when they say I am doing well, listen carefully for any problems they may know about but are not telling me. Breakfast arrives, porridge if we are lucky, the drugs-trolley, the pots of pills. At 8.30, the doctor's ward round. I am getting to know who they are, recognise familiar faces but do not know all their names. I always ask the same question – when can I have the drains out? They look at the bottle on the floor, bubbling less with each day as the torn lung begins to heal and say 'soon.' I'm like a child on a long car journey: 'Are we nearly there?' knowing full well we have ages to go.

One Friday morning, the 21st June, the doctors are late with the ward round. This morning is different, and as time passes we start murmuring. We are ready, but where are they? Twenty minutes after their usual time, the familiar noises can be heard down the corridor. The flock arrive, wheeling in a television set which they plug in, only just avoiding unplugging Eireen's heart monitor in the process. Today the doctor's attention is torn between the patients and England playing Brazil in the quarter-final of the World Cup. Our reviews are quicker than usual, as the doctors turn to cheer, commiserate and discuss the game. The television, clearly, wins.

More drugs, more tea. We are turned out onto our chairs for the nurses to change the beds. Then washing and dressing. A nursing assistant comes and helps, washes my back and, if I am extremely lucky, my hair. I decide what to wear today, choosing between near identical sets of baggy trousers and tee shirts. A long rest after the exertion of getting dressed. Mo brings news of his night, where he had supper, how he slept, to whom he talked on the telephone.

The post arrives. On my second day on the ward, I was besieged. Bouquets of flowers, cards, letters. I could not cope, I burst into tears. Beautiful flowers but there was nowhere to put them. Many of the cards said the same thing: we are delighted, it is such good news. Get well soon.

I was confused. 'Why are you so delighted and why is this good news?' I wanted to shout. Don't you all know how bloody awful I feel? It is terrible, I don't want this. Is this my punishment? Why doesn't someone say, 'Poor Diana, you poor thing, why do you of all people have to go through this?' It is ghastly, unfair. I wanted just then exactly what I had avoided all my life, people's compassion and pity. I had become a victim of my own success and fooled them all that I can cope with everything. I put the cards away in my locker. Later on, as the days went by and a semblance of sanity returned, I took them out again and read them one by one. Looked at the pictures, colours and textures of the cards, and cried, hearing the sentiments behind them. People were wishing me well. Sending me their love. I pictured my friends as a group of elephants surrounding one of their own who is injured, nudging it gently with their trunks, patting, get well, get well. Each card a nudge. And the letters, proper letters written on notepaper, words to make me laugh and cry. People wrote to tell me where they were, what they felt when they heard I'd had the transplant. Cath wrote, 'I was so thrilled to get your news, I could only think of dashing out and celebrating on your behalf by going shopping.' She sent me a set of pink nail-polishes to match my new, pink toes. My sister Annie told me, 'I was driving back from Street in Somerset on Sunday when I got your news. I was quite overcome, could hardly breathe let alone talk. I had to stop the car. It was so thrilling after your long wait and absolutely terrifying to think what you're going through.' My mother wrote: 'I can't put our relief and happiness into words.' The paper had marks of tears on it, but had a

PS, 'Don't start being too bossy too soon or the hospital will throw you out.'

The day revolves around medication. I had known all along that I would have to take a lot of drugs after the transplant. But I knew this as an abstract concept, not a hard reality. The hard reality comes in the shape of the drugs-trolley resembling the sweet trolley of my childhood at Brownie camp. Lots of colourful packets, dished out into small cups and offered with a smile. My little cups of pills arrive promptly at 8 am, 10 am, 12 noon, 2 pm, 6 pm, 8 pm and 10 pm. Each pot contains a different concoction depending on the time of day. I find the routine horrifying and dread each pot arriving. I work out tricks to get them down, listening to the radio to try and avoid noticing what I am doing, or shoving as many down as possible to reduce the number of swallows. The thought of having to do this for the rest of my life is too much to contemplate so I work on the basis of one pot at a time. I try not to see the drugs as nasty toxic poisons, but as little friends and helpers, enabling my new organs to 'bed down' and be accepted by the rest of my body. A large part of me wants to vomit them out and run.

The days progress. One of the transplant nurses comes to see me every day for my education session. I learn the nurse's names, their different styles. Celia, Cheryl, Carol, Val, Corrine. The apparently random sequence of pots of pills, intravenous infusions, inhalations, creams and potions, begins to make sense. After the transplant, it is necessary to suppress my immune system to stop my body rejecting the new organs. I learn about my drugs, what they are all for, their side-effects. First of all, three immunosuppressants. The main immunosuppressant, cyclosporin, was developed in the 1970s and comes in huge brown capsules, almost impossible to swallow. The stuff stinks. Cyclosporin is supplemented by mycophenolate mofetil, a newer immunosuppressant, thankfully smaller, purple pills, along with steroids, small white tablets of prednisolone, a handful of these. Everything seems to come in handfuls.

My suppressed immune system means I am open to any and all

passing infections, particularly while in hospital and particularly, I learn, when part of the hospital is a building-site. So I take antibiotics – several of these, with exotic names: aciclovir, an antiviral which I have to continue to take for the first three months; amphotericin, an anti-fungal for the spores circulating because of digging up old buildings, taken as a nebuliser twice a day, inhaled through a small machine that would not have looked out of place amongst the hookahs on the Edgware Road. I put anti-fungal cream up my nose and swish my mouth out with nystatin. Drugs to prevent the side-effects of the others. Anti-emetics to stop sickness. A lipid lowering statin drug, since the immunosuppressants cause cholesterol to rise. Medication to stop my blood pressure rising, another side-effect of the immunosuppressants. Calcium tablets to reduce bone loss while on steroids. Painkillers – paracetamol and tramadol. Ranitidine to protect my stomach, the other medications causing over-acidity which might cause ulcers. And, last thing at night, temazepam to help me sleep, although it does not seem to have very much effect other than making the night pass in a dopey haze.

And here was I, a proponent of alternative medicine, one who preferred to use homoeopathy as a first call when ill, reluctant to take even an aspirin, who had got to forty-six with a heart problem and was on only two medications, now swallowing forty or so pills a day, breathing in two nebulised infusions twice a day and submitting meekly to intravenous antibiotics. In the past I'd used complementary therapies, with varying results. At worst, some of them were probably of greater financial benefit to the practitioner than of medical benefit to me; others seemed to help, or at least gave me the illusion of doing something to help myself. But the research simply has not been done and their effects on people who have had transplants and interactions with other medications remain unknown. Many complementary therapies act to stimulate the immune system, not a desired effect in transplant patients. Some herbal remedies, such as St John's wort or Echinacea, may affect the action of immunosuppressants and are therefore dangerous. Although a homoeopath friend had assured me, before the transplant, that the way homoeopathy works could not possibly interact with medications, I did not want to be a guinea-pig. I'd be happy to try a spot of faith-healing, crystals or tantric sex, or indulge in the power of positive thinking, but my vials of homoeopathic remedies and jars of herbs and vitamins were to be consigned to history.

I learn, too, about the blue book, where I record all my medications, now and for ever. I am sad it is blue, a horrible shade of electric blue. I never wear blue, I like the colours of autumn, reds, greens, oranges, browns. The only blue I like is a deep peacock, the colour of my wedding jacket, and later the colour of a dress I wear to my 'first birthday' party, one year after the transplant. But blue it is. Blue, in return for a new life.

The day goes on. After lunch, we are allowed a nap. An hour's quiet time. We are tucked up in our beds, curtains drawn, lights out, visitors banned. I used to love my hour's nap at junior school, when we got blankets and cushions out of the cupboard and made beds for ourselves on the floor, a sea of giggling, snoring five-year-olds. I always slept, falling into dreaming sleep, the dreams of childhood. And now I sleep wrapped in white blankets on my hospital bed, snuggled, warm. One Monday I woke to find angels at the end of my bed, two white clothed figures murmuring softly. I put on my glasses and they metamorphosed into Peter Hopkins and John Wallwork. Professor Wallwork, the transplant service director, performed Papworth's first successful heart–lung transplant in 1984. Now he stands at the end of my bed, quickly reviewing the fruits of his labours. I asked them to sing for me. They laugh, but do not, on this occasion, oblige. Still, I suppose working miracles is good enough.

After the nap, we head into the long afternoon. More drugs. 'The Archers' on the radio. Visitors. I do not like visitors in hospital, do not feel I can cope with the attention, concern, being seen looking such a mess. I cannot talk very much, finding it hard to project my voice through my throat traumatised by the ventilation tube. I just want to see Mo. But I have phone calls. I talk to my parents, reassure them that I am okay although I do not feel it. I discover that the hospital call-box can be wheeled to my bed and phone friends to ask them to tell me news, gossip, tit-bits from the real world. I love to hear what they have been up to. 'Today, we went to the supermarket.' Imagine, being able to walk around a supermarket, feeling ordinary, without trailing a vacuum cleaner from the chest. One day, one day.

In the afternoon the dietician comes round to see me. I am presented with a list of do's and don'ts. Off the menu is anything that might harbour pestilence and disease: raw eggs, seafood, unwashed fruit and vegetables, unpasturised milk. Pâté, deli salads, blue cheeses, stilton, brie, Roquefort, camembert oozing across the plate, Danish blue bringing tears to the eyes. I watch my favourite picnic fly away. Luckily I feel too sick to care, but I will, later on. I also learn later on, to my relief, that the ban can be lifted on some of the foods after six months or so. But in the early stages I have to avoid getting upset stomachs which may interfere with the absorption of the immunosuppressant medication. I tell the dietician I am trying to eat but feel constantly nauseous and have no appetite. My weight has always been pretty low for a woman of nearly five foot nine, and it was now dropping. The dietician, a sweet kind soul whom I am always pleased to see, takes me under her wing and prescribes thick, sticky nutritious drinks and junk food – crisps, Pringles, salted biscuits, cheddars, anything high fat and high salt. I crunch and munch and manage to get something down on occasions.

More drugs, more tea, more chat. I still cannot read but if I am very lucky Mo reads to me, bits from the newspaper, a chapter or two of a John Grisham novel. Mo is tired, tired. He is bearing all the strain of it all. I send him home, back to the cats, to have some time out. I am terrified without him, but manage – I borrow other people's visitors to talk to, listen to the radio. My mother comes to visit and I want to burst into tears when I see her. She walks into the ward and when she sees me she starts crying, saying, 'I've got a new baby.' She cannot believe it. Her blue baby has turned pink. I show her my toes, forever blue, which are now creamy pink. My pink fingernails. We talk and talk. News and gossip from home, plans for me when I am well. We do the crossword. Mother and daughter. She tells me that whenever she had a wish, when she got the wishbone on the Sunday chicken, or had to blow out candles on her birthdays, she would wish for me to be well. Forty-six years of her wishes and it finally worked. Just over a year later, when celebrating her birthday, she is to look at me before blowing out the candle on her cake and whisper, 'I don't need to wish for you any more.'

Gradually, the tubes come out. The ones from my arms go quite soon, then my neck line, then some of the chest wires and drains. Finally, thirteen days after the operation, I come off the vacuum pump. I am terrified that my lung will collapse again, but I am reassured that it is unlikely; and even if it does happen, it is easily treatable. 'We just pop another drain in, under local anaesthetic,' explains the nurse. Easy. I go for twenty-four hours with just one chest drain. This time, untethered from the wall, I am mobile. Carrying my bottle in a long-handled basket I walk to the bathroom for the first time. I look in the mirror and a stranger looks back. My eyes are the same, but fewer wrinkles. I look like a porcelain doll, cream skin, pink, plump cheeks. Bushy eyebrows, unplucked for two weeks, unheard-of neglect. My lips are red. I stick out my tongue and admire my pink mouth. And use the toilet, a proper, sit-down visit. No more commodes. I wash and wash, leave the tap running, listen to the water, imagine washing it all away. I get my tweezers and tidy myself up, put on my make up, humanise and sanitise myself. Like a vain teenager I stay in the bathroom for ages until the nurse, concerned, knocks on the door.

I set off round the ward. I look for the fish-tank, remembering that night I came in, thirteen year-long days ago. The side-ward where I waited is now full of men lying on beds in striped pyjamas, whiling away the time. My legs wobble and shake but I do not get out of breath. I try and walk faster to test my new apparatus and feel violent nausea. Back to the bathroom to retch, then another walk. The nurses warn me to take it slowly, come back, rest.

On Sunday, two weeks after the operation, Mo is back, only a little refreshed, full of news from home – how the cats are, chats with the neighbours. Someone has mown the lawn for us, everyone sends good wishes. He brings my emails, telephone messages, a slice of normality. We set off for our first walk, with a wheelchair in case I get tired, and head for the pond. I've listened to the ducks for nearly two weeks and want to meet my serenaders. Drakes, great crested grebes, mallards. Common Shelducks and tufted ducks. Moorhens fussing around tiny, darting babies. A solitary black swan. Messy, noisy barnacle geese, the odd Carolina wood duck outshining the rest. We sit on a bench by the pond, the sun on our faces. I realise I have survived.

10. Going Home
25th June–31st July 2002

AFTER BEING IN HOSPITAL for sixteen days, I am to be discharged to the hospital flat before going home. At last I am considered well enough to be away from the watchful eyes of nurses, doctors, blood-pressure monitors, observation routines. I have to bargain my way out. Once the final drain is removed, I am raring to go. I want to sleep with my husband. Not rampant sex – not rampant anything, not with a chest reduced to a battlefield, the threat of throwing up with too much motion, skin that feels as if it will jump out of itself with the slightest touch, muscles aching from disuse – but quiet comfort, warmth, familiarity, knowing that I can just be myself and not have to be a good patient, a patient patient. I want to be free to eat what I want and when and make my own tea, Darjeeling, not too strong, not too weak, the right temperature, the right colour. I want to make phone calls, to sit in a quiet room. I've missed Mo – this is the longest we've been sleeping separately for twelve years, our bodies now designed to fit into each other throughout the night. I hope that sleep will come when my teddy-bear is at my side. As soon as the doctors come round on Sunday morning, I make my request.

'I'm fine. Can I go now?'

They confer, and look at the charts, and ask how I am managing with the medication, the observations, the dietary rules, the exercise. Eventually they answer: 'No.' Not yet.

'You need to see how you get on down at the gym,' Peter says. 'We need a few more blood results, then we'll see. Maybe Wednesday.'

'How about Tuesday then?' I am pushing my luck, but worth a try.

More discussions, conferring. 'Okay, but we'll see how you are.'

Having arranged to go to the flat on Tuesday, I am terrified. How will I cope? What if I get so sick I cannot stop? What if my chest comes open in the middle of the night? The hospital suddenly seems so attractive, familiar, ordinary. I talk to one of the nurses, who reassures me that I can come back into hospital if I need to.

'We are just next door,' she says. 'Someone will always be available, you just need to phone.' The nurses on Mallard Ward have become friends over the past two weeks. They are familiar. I've heard their stories, their jokes. I have learned which ones to ask for different things – who likes to chat, who will bring an extra cup of tea. We've shared a few laughs. I'll miss them, but I decide to go, if possible.

Monday morning brings new challenges. My first trip to the gym. Most patients go there as few as five days after a transplant, but my tubes and drains have held me back, so I have been deprived of the pleasure, watching my fellow patients go, then return, pale faced, to sit quietly and contemplate their newly found muscles. When the porter comes to collect me, I want to walk down but am told in no uncertain terms to sit in the wheelchair and reserve my energy for the gym. We go in a fleet, collecting patients from side rooms and other wards as we go. I meet a young man who has been in hospital for five months following complications with a lung transplant. Two men who have had new hearts. A woman, older than me, with two new lungs and a bout of deep depression. The procession rumbles and moans along to the gym, swapping horror stories of things going wrong, problems with drugs, pains, aches, infections. I try and turn off my mind, not wanting to be reminded of what might yet happen. I feel at the end of my resources. I am just about managing so long as nothing else goes wrong. I start to feel sick, with waves of nausea from head to toe. I want to go back to my bed, but make myself smile and decide to carry on. What if I vomit in the gym? I guess they must be used to it, they will have a basin, towels, water.

At the gym we meet Melanie and Sam, jolly, smiley physiotherapists who talk us through the routine. We are told how our new hearts work. We learn that our new organs no longer have intact nerve connections to the rest of the body. In the case of the heart, these nerve connections cause the heart to speed up when we exercise. In the absence of nerve impulses, the heart simply does not know to get going when we start to move; hence, if we suddenly sit up or walk fast, we feel dizzy because the heart remains at resting rate. When we have been moving for a few minutes, the muscles start to release catecholamines, chemical messengers which are transmitted through the blood telling the heart to speed up. So we are advised to warm up slowly when exercising, at least until the new heart has got used to getting messages from the muscles rather than the brain. We are told, too, that our lungs are a bit slow to catch on to exercise. Once lungs are transplanted, they are missing the nerves telling us to breathe faster when we start to move. Now, when we start to exercise, our muscles need more oxygen: but rather than automatically beginning to breathe more deeply, we remain breathing at the same rate as when at rest, and tire very quickly. Hence the need for deliberate heavy breathing to begin with.

'Let's warm up,' shouts Melanie. 'Take some deep breaths, in and out, in and out.' We groan and mutter as we gasp in and out against the pressure of scar tissue, wiring, stitches.

'Good,' she cries. 'Now start walking on the spot. One two, one two. Good. Now a little bit faster.'

John, who is in his sixties and has spent four weeks in hospital, sits down, muttering.

'I can't do this, it hurts,' he says.

'Stop moaning and get on with it,' exclaims Sam. 'Up and on.' We laugh, nervously, but are full of admiration for John as he rises to the challenge and gets on.

We go through our warm-up routine – marching on the spot,

squatting, stretching. Stepping up and down. Getting our new hearts and lungs working. I progress to the treadmill and spend five minutes walking. A little faster than I've walked for years. My muscles groan and shake, my mind forces them on. This is to be the first of a long battle between my mind willing me on and my body, conditioned for years into slowness and inactivity, now being urged to go beyond its capabilities. I am a bundle of pain, of sickness, but I squat, walk, march. I do everything I have spent years avoiding – I push myself, get slightly out of breath – but it doesn't feel anything like the breathlessness I am used to. I arrive back at the ward, vomiting, retching, shaking, unable to summon the energy to climb back into bed, but triumphant. I've been to the gym.

Helen comes to tell me that my blood tests that day show that I am severely anaemic and the level of cyclosporin in my blood is far too high. The levels of the immunosuppressants are measured regularly since they can fluctuate wildly in the first few weeks. Helen laughs when I tell her I've been to the gym and now feel sick. 'I'm not surprised,' she says. 'It's a wonder you're on your feet at all. We'll give you a blood transfusion and cut the cyclosporin and you'll be fine tomorrow.'

The next day, after a sleepless night being transfused with someone else's blood, I am not fine but keep quiet so I can get out of the hospital. We are to stay in the flat available to transplant patients, in the top half of a 1950s detached house just up the road from the hospital. It reminds me of an apartment I stayed in when I visited New Zealand for a year in 1982, old-fashioned, worn but comfortable. This is to be home for the next few days. We try a few normal activities. We go to the local towns: St Ives, St Neots, Huntingdon. I cannot taste, I feel strange, shaky, nauseous, but we go through the motions of morning coffee, lunch, afternoon tea. I am not really here at all and expect people to gasp when they see me, the leper in the midst, but I seem to be invisible. 'Do you know what I've been through?' I want to say. 'I'm not like you any more, with your own bits. I'm now two people really.' Someone knocks into me, his elbow in my chest, and I double up. We go back to the flat, cook pizza and watch television.

At night I can sleep with Mo again. We hold hands, curl our legs together, whisper in the dark. He is so, so tired. All the attention has been on me, but what about him? Mo is coping in the way he always does. He puts his head down and gets on with whatever needs to be done. I make him talk, tell me what it has been like for him, but he cannot begin to say. That is to come much later.

Each day I go to the gym with the other transplant patients, to go through our routines. It never feels any easier but I am amazed at what I can do. I progress from the treadmill to the exercise bicycle and pedal for a few minutes. This exercise bike is much harder than the one at the end of my bed in the ward. I realise they fix them depending on the abilities of the patient: ward patients have the special, easy ones. Once in the gym, we have to work. I'm often sick after the gym but keep going. A lifetime of keeping going.

After only four days in the flat, it is time to go home. We see Peter in the clinic on Friday morning and he is happy for us to go. I am not happy and want to stay. We have to come back the following Tuesday so I ask him, can't we stay over the weekend?

'You have to go home sometime,' he tells me. 'You need to get away from here and try out your new life.'

'I don't really feel ready. What if something goes wrong? I'll be miles away.' I want to whinge, moan, be reassured.

'You can phone anytime. There's always someone here. Off you go now.' I am dismissed.

And so we go home. We pack up my mountains of clothes, food we have bought to try and tempt my appetite, books, magazines, presents I've been given, flowers, cards. I cannot lift, am not allowed to use my arms for three months while my sternum heals, so Mo carries bag after bag of my stuff out to the car. We drive off and head for home. I've been away for just under three weeks, but I might as well have been living on another planet for years. Everything seems alien, as though I am seeing it for the first time. We stop at my parents' house on the outskirts of Oxford. My father, seeing me for the first time since the operation, does not know what to say. He just looks at me, astounded. I can see he is moved, amazed at the change in me, but cannot speak.

When we get home, it all looks strangely familiar but very different. I was expecting to feel happy, delighted, relieved, but instead feel flat and disappointed and anxious. 'What-ifs' run riot around my head and I feel adrift, away from the people that can make it better. Ann and Anthony come round to say hello, and I feel I cannot cope with normal people. I am still at the hospital being a patient and they are seeing me as Diana. How can I possibly be Diana to them if I do not know who I am, if I am still me after all this? They bring around a meal for us and I force down as much as possible. My first night in my own bed, which should have been a delight, is a nightmare. I cannot get comfortable, organising and reorganising pillows in order to try and sleep on my back, which I can never get used to, and my anxiety hits the roof at about 3 am. I want to sob but am too tired to manage more than a whimper. Mo stays awake with me, calming, reassuring, bringing drinks, getting pillows. I fall asleep about 4 am, only to wake up an hour later screaming as a heavy load falls onto my sternum and pain shoots all over my body. My little cat, Smog, who loves to sleep on my chest, has jumped onto her favourite place.

The next day I sit in the garden and try and look through some of my post. My eyes are still not working properly and I cannot concentrate on the cards, letters, bills and junk mail that have arrived over the past weeks. Suddenly nausea strikes, waves and waves of nausea and vomiting. I rush to the bathroom and stay there for two hours. We call Papworth, who prescribe ondansetron, a strong and very expensive anti-emetic. We cannot find a chemist who stocks it and I have to wait until the next day. When I try it, the nausea recedes – a welcome relief. However, the following day the nausea comes back, with retching and vomiting, and this time the medication does not work. We limp through the next few days and nights and arrive at Tuesday, when we can return to Papworth. We get up at 6 am and drive through the traffic, arriving at the hospital to start the clinic routine.

The outpatient schedule is always the same. First I go to have my lung function measured. Smiley technicians take me through a routine of blowing into tubes to measure peak flow, total lung volume, total expiration, saturation. 'Blow blow blow blow blow,' they call, encouraging the patient until red in the face. I puff and gasp, my lungs straining and objecting, my scar tearing, in order to get better and better results. Before the operation, my lung capacity measured as forced expired volume (FEV1), the volume of air that can be breathed out in one second, was 1.60, significantly lower than normal; now it has gone up to 3.15 and later, after months of exercise, expands to a 4.00, described by one of the doctors as 'awesome'. After blow-blow-blowing, off to the clinic for blood tests. I get to know the phlebotomists. Derek tells me of his holidays in the Maldives and his love for cross-country running; Ruth shares my enthusiasm for Greece and makes me teach her a Greek word or two as needle plunges in. They are expert at distraction at the moment of sharp pain, optimistically described as 'just as scratch'. My blood pressure, weight, oxygen saturation are measured by the nurses, who send me for an X-ray. In, out, take a deep breath, hold it and breathe away. I have long lungs, I learn, and cannot fit on a normal-size screen. Then back to the outpatient department to wait to see the doctor.

I realise the wait is deliberate because of the amount of time it gives for patients to talk to each other, to find common ground and swap horror stories. I meet up again with two of the men I'd met in the gym and we discuss our progress. I am exhausted, sick, shaky, finding it difficult to cope, but none of this I admit. I know I am doing well, have got out of hospital early, have not experienced problems with infection or rejection and really have nothing to worry about. So we are cheerful and hide our struggles. We are grateful to be the ones who have made it.

After some time, we get to see Peter. I have brought along a list of problems. Peter is pleased.

'Right, read them all out and I'll prepare my counter-attack,' he says.

Celia, the senior nurse who runs the transplant clinic, comes in with me when I see Peter. The clinic nurses must have heard every problem in the book and they always seem to have some kind of answer, which is just as well – in the six months after the transplant, I am forever ringing them up with my questions. Between them, Celia and Peter sort out the list I bring. I tell them about the nausea and vomiting and how nothing so far seems to work. Peter prescribes another anti-emetic, metoclopramide. I describe the shaking, constant tremors that make it difficult to write or hold a cup of tea and Celia says that this will get better over the next couple of months, and that they will reduce my dose of cyclosporin. I talk about tiredness, weakness, pains on exercise, and they recommend that I talk again to the physiotherapists to work out a plan. I tell Peter my concerns about my lungs suddenly collapsing again and he reassures me that I would need a stab wound or skiing accident for that to happen and tells me to stop watching hospital dramas on TV. I talk about my insomnia – lying awake all night, unable to sleep – and he recommends that I take zopiclone. It seems that my problems do have solutions.

'I know it is a very difficult time,' Peter says. 'Our job is to get you through the first three months, then we can start reducing the doses. By three months you've done a lot of healing. It does get easier.' I find this heartening. I no longer have to do it all on my own: Papworth is alongside me, giving me a hand.

'You'll need to come back next week for a fibreoptic bronchoscopy, so we can check how things are going. There are some slight risks …'

He begins to explain but I interrupt him.

'Is this something I have to have?'

He tells me it is.

'I don't want to know the risks or what might happen,' I reply. 'I'd prefer not to know.' I'm surprised to hear myself say this. Most of my life I'd wanted to be fully informed about medical procedures and go in with my eyes open. Now, keeping them firmly shut seems the better option.

'That's fine,' Peter says. 'If there are any problems we'll deal with them.'

I go back home and try the new regime. I am concerned about starting to take sleeping-pills. In my work as a psychologist, I had seen some of the problems caused by tranquillisers and tried to help people withdraw from them. I know what I have to do to tackle my own insomnia: go to bed and get up at a set time. If I cannot sleep, then get up, do something different, wait until I felt sleepy before going back to bed. Do not worry about not sleeping, it is not damaging or permanent. However, I have been feeling awful, the days seem interminable, and now to be awake for twenty-four hours at a time seems unmanageable. I am desperate to get some sleep. So I start the zopiclone. And it works.

At last I know that however bad each day is, I can get some relief. About twenty minutes after taking the pill, my mind drifts off into dreams and I sleep for about six hours, then a couple more. I have some rest. I do not feel much better for it during the day, but can look forward to some time off during the night.

We limp through another week, trying to get by, pass the time as best as possible. I try to do something every day, a tiny walk, a visit from my parents, seeing a few friends. I sit in the garden feeling sick, shaky, trying to be cheerful, willing time to pass. The start of months of willing the time to pass.

I went back to Papworth for the bronchoscopy. I was not particularly concerned about it, but something must have been preying on my mind. I did not come round from the anaesthetic until two hours later, and when I woke up, a couple of doctors from the transplant team were standing at the end of the bed laughing. They told me that, after I'd been given the knock-out dose, I sat up, wide awake, looked accusingly at Peter and demanded to know how many of these biopsies he had done before. 'About forty thousand,' he told me, and I promptly lay down and went to sleep. To stop me getting any more uppity, I got extra sedation.

Peter came to tell me the results.

'It all looked beautiful,' he said. 'Beautiful.' Later I tell Cath of my beautiful bronchoscopy.

'Well,' she exclaimed. 'Now you know you've got inner beauty!'

Inner beauty I may have, but outer beauty was alluding me. I had turned into a fat-faced hairy monster. 'Moon face,' 'Charlie Brown face,' 'chipmunk,' 'hamster,' whatever the effect is called, steroids cause the lower cheeks and jaw to swell and round out like a baby. It affects different people to varying degrees and depends on the dose of steroids. When we were staying in the hospital flat, I took some pictures of myself in the photo-booth in the St Ives branch of Woolworth's. I looked about nine or ten, a round baby face, my wrinkles disappearing as tissues plumped out with the steroids. A few months later, as the dose was reduced down to 10 mg prednisolone, my face was less baby-like but remained rounder, fuller. When I saw people for the first time, they would comment on my appearance. Most would say I looked very well, but some people were painfully direct. One pinched my face, exclaiming 'Chubby cheeks!' while another told me what a shock she got when she saw me, my face looked so different.

I am not sure why she had to tell me how I made her feel. I am not sure, also, why the process of having a transplant gave people permission to make such personal comments. If I had simply put on weight, I would not expect people to comment on it so blatantly and certainly would not do so myself to someone else. But a transplantee is seen as fair game – after all, the changes are for the greater good. However, I found the process of comments and exclamations quite an ordeal. I had lived with my face for nearly half a century and suddenly it was different – rounder, softer, pinker. I didn't like it much, even hated it at times, and longed to have my old familiar face back again.

Hair was another problem. Three weeks after the transplant I noticed fine white down appearing over my face and neck. Later it grew thicker and developed into a full-blown moustache. I also developed thick sideburns and hair on my chin. I had grown a beard.

The hair on my arms became luxuriant, and long dark hairs sprouted on my thighs. Being fair, I'd never been particularly hairy. I had put off doing anything about the hairs on my legs until I was forty, resisting my sister's invitations to join them in the bathroom for a communal shave or wax when we were teenagers. I was quite proud of my hairy legs until I mentioned to a friend my plan to leave well alone. Her look of disapproval led me to the waxing-salon the next day. But now hair was growing everywhere. I was horrified. Transplant, yes. Beard, no.

I bemoaned my hairiness at length, neurotically, with Jacky and Cath who were polite and dismissive, saying it was invisible, but my honest friend Anna exclaimed, 'It's lovely! You look like a little kitten!'

Mo said he did not notice it at all: but he gave the game away later, when – after the hair had disappeared – he said he could no longer feel my moustache tickling him when we kissed. I discussed my hirsutism at my next visit to Papworth, who explained that it was a well known side-effect of cyclosporin and that I could change to tacrolimus, a newer immunosuppressant with different side-effects. I swapped without hesitation.

It took a couple of months for anything to happen to my beard: then one day it was gone. I looked for it on my pillow, round the house, but no sign. The hair must have washed off, I decided, but even now I remain slightly nervous about it leaping out at me one day from the back of a cupboard.

Somehow my unfamiliar face and I had to get on with our new life together, with a new set of rules for living – how to manage my transplant, what might go wrong, how to detect early signs of rejection or infection, what to eat, what to do, what to think. I learned, in short, to be terrified. I was given so much information about potential problems that they soon became actual terrible realities in my mind.

My main fear was of rejection. I knew all about rejection. Starting at the age of ten with Hughie, the son of the farmers who owned a holiday cottage in Wales in which we spent a wet Easter. Twelve-year-old Hughie was set up by my sisters to meet me in the barn and give me a romantic, passionate kiss. We briefly, embarrassedly, wrestled and I was honoured with a quick peck on the cheek before he ran away blushing. I decided this was love and set out to woo him, but he avoided me for the rest of the holiday. I was mortified. Then in my teens, I fell deeply in love with a beautiful blond young man at my drama class. I decided the way to get noticed was to be miserable, sit in corners looking pale and interesting, occasional sobs coming from my soul. He rose to the bait and asked once or twice, 'All right?' before making off with my irrepressibly cheerful schoolfriend, admittedly much better endowed than me. Again, I was mortified and in a quandary of rejected self-doubt for weeks. More rejections, as well as successes, followed, but none quite measured up to the pain of losing my first love.

The rejection I now had to be wary of involved my own body ganging up on my new organs and trying to destroy them, a process that starts the moment of transplant and carries on for life. The body's immune system looks after us by attacking anything that it regards as foreign: it recognises and destroys viruses, infections or any rogue cells from the body which are threatening to grow out of control.

Unfortunately, the same mechanism recognises the new organs as foreigners. There are three different types of rejection. 'Hyperacute' rejection can occur within minutes of a transplant. If the recipient has a large number of antibodies that react with the donor organs, or if the donor's blood type is incompatible with the recipient, the recipient body makes very clear it wants nothing to do with these new organs. This is almost unheard of, since donor and recipient are carefully matched on blood group. 'Acute' rejection occurs when the recipient's immune-system T cells recognise the donor organs as foreign and start to respond. Acute rejection is most common in the first six months after a transplant, but can also occur later on, particularly if the levels of immunosuppressant medication fall too low. 'Chronic' rejection is a complex process that involves both antibodies and lymphocytes and causes problems such as atherosclerosis, or hardening of the arteries, in transplanted hearts, and bronchiolitis obliterans, or scarring, in transplanted lungs. The frequency and degree of rejection vary enormously – I have met people have a lot of problems during the first year or so and others, like myself, who have never, as yet, had any episodes.

Unlike matters of love, organ rejection can be treated with medication. Immunosuppressant medication is constantly improving as each new generation is developed. However, transplant patients are always at risk of rejection and we need to monitor carefully for early signs and symptoms. Indications of acute rejection include a rise in temperature, sudden weight gain, decrease in lung function, feeling fluey or out of sorts, low energy, chest pains. If these changes occurred, I would have another bronchoscopy to confirm whether acute rejection was present and if so, large doses of steroids to settle everything down. Some of the signs could be monitored objectively, and either were or were not present. The other indications were vague enough to allow the worried mind to seek out symptoms and magnify them. I had to be vigilant and let the transplant team know immediately things started to go amiss. However, how was I to know what to look for? I felt awful anyway, hot and cold, achy, low in energy and thoroughly despondent. I had to trust that religious monitoring of my temperature, weight and lung function would be enough to pick up any rejection.

Infection, public enemy number two for transplant patients, was another story. Reduce the immune system, increase the risk of infection. Living in a hospital for over two weeks, I was surrounded by bugs, germs, viruses, bacteria, dirt and horrors unbounded. I could almost see them flying through the air like a swarm of bees. When I came home, I took one look at the cats and their dirty paws, a minefield of disease, covered with dried saliva from constant washing, and panicked. The transplant nurses' opinion had been divided: one, a cat-lover, told me to treat them as normal, but to take extra care with litter-trays. Another had said it was like stroking used toilet paper. I started to wash my hands after stroking the cats only to realise how daft that was – I wanted to get back to a normal life as soon as possible and that meant taking some risks.

But what risks to take, how much to do? I didn't know. I had to start the long process of finding out what my new body was capable of, how to look after myself. Start living my life again.

My priority at that time was to eat, sleep and exercise. Each morning, having taken one set of pills, forced down breakfast, got up, taken another lot of pills and remembered not to clean my teeth immediately because I risked throwing up and not absorbing the pills, I got to work on my legs. I strapped weights round my ankles and bent and stretched my complaining legs, lifted and raised, pushed and pulled to try and build up a few muscles. We went for walks, first to the end of the road, then to the end of the road twice, then round the block. We drove to the park and walked in a gradually increasing circle, watching green woodpeckers, each day setting slightly further targets. We walked in Brasenose Woods and Shotover Country Park, round the University Parks, Cutteslowe, South Park, Headington Hill Park. Each walk was a mixture of excruciating pain and achievement. I breathed deeply, swinging my arms, pushing my legs which screamed in protest at unaccustomed forces, wobbling along. I set tiny goals to keep going. I just have to walk to that tree, then the next one, then to that clump of grass, then the next one, on and on until we had covered the required ground and I could rest.

I tried to go through the motions of doing things, occasionally going into a shop, worried about seeing so many people in case they passed on their bugs and germs to me, flying straight at my suppressed immune system. Friends came round, Cath reminding me that I had to keep going, try and distract myself as much as possible, Jacky encouraging me, telling me that time will pass, it will get better. My family, too, bringing food, jokes, love.

Somehow I kept going. Getting through each day. The next months were a haze of adjustment and risks, practising, experimenting, trying it all out. Re-learning the rules. And the first rule, I found out, was that things had to get a lot worse before they could start to get better.

11. Running Away
August to mid-October 2002

LOOKING BACK ON THE WHOLE experience, I realise that having a transplant involves five stages: getting ill, making the decision to have the transplant, going on the waiting-list, having the operation and then finally, recovery.

When I was in each of these stages, I believed it was the worst one. I believed that once I had got through whatever phase I was in, somehow the next would be more manageable. I went through a process of mental bargaining which at the time seemed to help. 'I'm getting through this and I know that this is the worst it will get,' I would tell myself. 'It'll be easier to cope once this stage is at the end.' The operation and its aftermath were the aspects of the whole experience I chose to think of the least, relegated to a category in my mind, 'I'll deal with that when I come to it.' If anything, I expected recovery to be swift and painless, guided by the words of the transplant team, that some people are able to go back to work shortly afterwards, that some people feel fine, that many feel so much better for getting rid of the troublesome parts. I expected to be delighted to be one of the chosen few, delighted to have the transplant over at last. I was completely wrong.

In fact the challenges got progressively more difficult over the four months after the transplant. They weren't helped by my feelings of disillusionment, and my strong sense that I was being kicked when down. With my heart condition, I was dealing with a progressive disease, so things were by definition likely to get worse over time. And of course surgery is a major challenge to body and soul, so the idea that dealing with the operation would be the easiest phase was somewhat misguided. Because now I realise that a transplant is not a cure, but a swap – an exchange of one set of problems for another, hopefully lesser, set of problems. The initial problem was coping with the first few months.

I didn't cope. I was sick, violently, intermittently sick for four months. I felt toxic, dreaded swallowing the pills then battling to keep them down. I lost any semblance of appetite I may have had, feeling nauseated by food but worse, dead and flat. I could have been in the middle of the most gorgeous, appetising foods, all my favourites – runny, smelly cheeses, fresh breads, ripe mangoes, strawberries and cream, olives, Christmas cake, avocadoes, cherries, marmite soldiers – and remain completely indifferent. They all looked and tasted like cardboard. I grieved the loss of my appetite like parting with an old friend. I had to eat to stay alive, I had to try and put on the weight lost during the surgery and subsequent vomiting – gaining weight, I was assured, would help my body cope better with the drugs. One of the dieticians at Papworth had said, incongruously, that I had to eat, but it would be like 'shovelling shit'. So I shovelled and forced food down, dividing each plate of food into half, eating that half, then dividing it again in half, eating that half, dividing and eating again down to the last mouthful. I was later to discover this working by halves, or 'pyramids', in body-conditioning classes in the gym, where we had to do sixteen, then eight, then four then two repetitions of gruelling exercises involving a step, hand-weights, sweat and lycra.

I went through the motions of living, walking, sleeping, seeing friends, with no enjoyment and no sense of achievement. Nothing I did made me feel any better, but I carried on, pushing myself to keep going, will power inside me combining forces with my fighting spirit to put one leg in front of the other, chew another, then another, mouthful of food, get through another day. Very occasionally I would have a good day. Then, I could see the future and remember that I would, soon, be able to go out on my own, walk for miles, swim without going blue, go to Greece, New Zealand. Six weeks after the transplant, I began to feel a bit better: less sick and shaky, a little more hopeful. But then after a few good days I plunged back downwards, the nausea returning with a vengeance, my spirits sinking again, made worse somehow by my having had a glimpse of normality before it vanished again.

Mo, on my bad days, did not leave me alone for longer than a few minutes. He sat with me, made me meals, took me out for walks, reminded me to take things one hour at a time, held my hand, gave me his love. Friends urged me on, saying, 'It's early days,' or 'It's only been a few weeks,' but to me it all seemed much longer. I did not know how long I was going to feel so bad, whether the sickness would ever end, whether my body would ever get used to the drugs. My sense of time was distorted so that each day felt like an eternity.

I tried to put on a brave face, but inside it all felt very different. My head was stuffed first with cotton wool, then with dark thoughts – the snake-pit of the mind let loose. I knew what I should be feeling, what I had expected to feel – relief that the wait was over, exhilaration that I had survived, excitement at a new future ahead and deep gratitude to my donor and to the hospital for making it all possible. Instead I was obsessed with questioning, over and over, whether I had made the right decision. Part of me believed that I was never meant to live, that this was my punishment. I was haunted by the fact that I had chosen this path, brought it upon myself. I longed for what I saw as the good old days when I sat at home on oxygen, able to read, write, enjoy gossiping with friends, watching a video. I knew what the rules were then; now I had no idea. How much should I be doing? What should I be doing to get better? Was I doing all right? Was this expected? Not knowing the answers, not knowing the future, my mood was dropping to deep depression.

I knew all about depression. I had worked with depressed people during my career. I knew the path out of depression, one tiny step at a time: planning the day, keeping a routine, doing enjoyable things, seeing negative thinking as simply distorted and unhelpful thoughts, not realities. Yes, I knew all this, but could neither recognise it in myself, nor summon the strength or wisdom to do anything about it. Gradually, my mind became consumed with ways of ending it all.

I felt deeply guilty for feeling like this – after all, my donor was dead and had never had a choice. How would my donor's family feel if they knew what I was thinking? Knowing that only made me worse, feel less and less worthy. I knew I had to get out, but how? I had enough medication to die several times over, but knew if I tried an overdose I would only be sick and that would not work. I thought about the impact it would have on other people if I did something dramatic, like hanging myself or jumping from a bridge, and I knew I did not want to ruin other lives. Ironically, I did not see my disappearance as too much of a problem for others – they would all be better off without me being around as such a misery-guts, and they must have been prepared for me dying anyway, so it would not come as too much of a shock. Mo would be relieved that I was not suffering any more and he'd be free to find some healthy woman who wouldn't be so much trouble. He'd thank me in the end for giving him an escape route.

Such was the painful distortion of my thoughts.

I was, in fact, suffering from shock and from the effects of steroids. A complex mental and physical adjustment to a major operation, which meant I had to rewrite all the rules I had been living my life with for forty-six years, while being, in effect, poisoned by the medication. This, at the time, I could not see. But one day, I suddenly saw the truth. I was sitting on the loo, in our tiny cloakroom under the stairs, when I realised I was walking around with the way out but hadn't recognised it. If the medication was making me feel so bad, then all I had to do was stop taking it. I would feel even worse as my body rejected my new heart and lungs, but, I presumed, I would eventually die. And that was my liberation. Sitting long after my bladder had emptied, I worked out that this was my choice, my absolute right if

I chose to do it. If, in the cold light of day and with a sane mind, I decided to stop taking the pills, there was nothing anyone could do. Sure, they could try to invoke the Mental Health Act and force me to take the medication, a scenario I was only too familiar with from my work, but I knew exactly what to say to convince anyone of my sanity. My six-year-old self, standing listening at the door, hands on hips, indignant, pouting, was calling me to stand up to these horrid doctors making me do all these horrid things.

And then realising I had this choice, I knew that I was not ready to take it. If I'd managed to survive the operation, to get through this far, somehow, then I could keep going a bit longer. On my walks, I always got to the next tree and the next and then the next. I could keep going to the next month, the next and the next. I remembered all the things people had said to me. My brother Rob sat on the bed one day stroking my head and holding my hand after I'd spent a night of severe sickness. I was exhausted and, crying pitifully, told him I didn't know how to keep going, I just wanted it all to be over.

'It's all part of a process,' he told me. 'A process, you just have to get through it. You're in the middle of something, so it must have an end. Just keep going.' My GP had come to visit me one Saturday afternoon, when sickness and exhaustion led to severe giddiness and I could not move my head without throwing up. I told him, tearfully, pathetically, that I regretted what I'd done, I wished I'd never had the operation. He looked at me thoughtfully, and said: 'Tell me that in a year's time. It is very difficult at the moment. It will probably carry on being difficult for some time longer. But then it will get better. You'll get better.' One day, full of sickness, I told Celia, the district nurse who visited me regularly throughout my illness and recovery, how hard it was to keep going.

'You'll be okay,' she said. 'I know it. You'll get through, with all the love from other people.'

Everyone was telling me that there was an end to this phase, I just didn't know when it would be. Most people said that six months and a year are milestones in terms of progress. I was curious enough to find out what it would be like for me. So, I decided that, if things were not better in a year, then I'd think again about whether to stop. My fighting spirit had returned. I got off the loo, looked myself in the mirror and said, 'Sod it, Diana. You can do it.'

I did not feel immediately better, but was liberated from the responsibility each day of having to decide not only what to wear, what to eat, what to do, but also whether to live or not. I hit dark spots, got through them and tried to start each day as a new one. I knew I had to just get on with it, so I did.

*   *   *

During my darkest months, I went back into hospital twice to sort out the drugs and find a combination that I could tolerate and keep down. The first time was after twenty-four hours of severe retching where sipping water, breathing, movement, would make me vomit uncontrollably. I had exhausted the expertise of the GP's deputising services throughout the night and both Mo and I were at the end of our tether. We packed our bags and drove to Papworth at dawn, collapsing when we got there, in need of looking after for a few days. The ward was dominated by a television set giving news of the disappearance of two young girls in a small village near Papworth. Our own problems moved onto another scale of measured awfulness as we watched the parents struggling to find out what had happened to their daughters, the pain of Soham village coping with its loss under the media spotlight and the speculation and sympathy of the country.

During my week in hospital my drug dosages reduced significantly, producing at least some hope of future respite. I was able to eat again, I got lots of advice about how to manage, what to do. Lots of encouragement that I was doing well. But most important for me were the people I met on the ward and what they taught me. Margaret, in her eighties, was in the bed opposite me. She had been admitted to hospital with a severe rash and difficulty breathing. She told me about her attempts to find out what it was and how she had been perplexing the medics for some time.

'You know, no one could say what it was,' she explained to me. 'No one. Then the last time I was in hospital one of the doctors, just a young one, said he'd seen another patient with what I've got. I got him to write it down for me and I looked it up on the internet. And there I was, just the same. It's a wonderful thing, the internet. I just don't know how we managed before it.'

I also met Sebrina, a tough young woman facing multiple surgery, multiple problems with her health, in and out of hospital against a history of abuse during her childhood, who kept on going throughout it all, believing that every cloud has a silver lining. She got knocked down over and over again, but each time would pick herself up and go on, now planning to go back to education after years of illness.

These people put my own difficulties into perspective. Many times during my stays in hospital I have felt humbled at what people are able to achieve. Not the Nobel prizewinners, but people who manage their lives courageously, humorously, while living alongside crippling and distressing medical problems. These are not the people anyone notices or shouts about, but people like Margaret and Sebrina have far more impact on me than those who win prizes.

The second time I went into hospital, again after uncontrollable vomiting, I met two people who made me realise just how incredibly lucky I had been. During my wait for the operation, I'd spoken on the telephone to Michael, whose lungs had been damaged as a child in a house fire and who now, in his forties, needed a transplant due to progressive lung disease. He, like me, was waiting for a heart and lung transplant. His own heart was in good condition, but technically a heart–lung transplant would have been easier than lungs alone. So his own healthy heart could then be used in a live-donor, or 'domino,' transplant for another recipient. Michael had always been hopeful, optimistic, looking forward to the day when he could breathe, aiming to, at last, go dancing with his wife. During my stay, Michael was also in Papworth for treatment of lung complications. Although I was feeling awful, I realised at least I had got another chance, whereas for Michael and many others their chance had not yet come. We sat in the day room and chatted, but the gulf between us was enormous – me on one side, being given my new life, Michael still waiting, uncertain that it would ever come. In fact, for Michael, it never did. He had many attempts at the transplant, but each time something was wrong, either with the donor organs or with him and he was sent home again. He did eventually have a transplant, but his health had deteriorated so much by then that he died three months later.

I met, also, Pauline, who had a very similar heart condition to my own. She had done reasonably well up until her late fifties, and by the time her health had deteriorated, she was told that she was unsuitable for a transplant. Her heart was failing and she was experiencing severe oedema, her legs and body swelling, her organs failing. Over the course of a few days, she became increasingly unwell until, angry, exhausted and in terrible pain, she died. It was so distressing for her family, but I felt that death had been a relief to Pauline in the end. And it was especially sobering for me in that I saw, in Pauline, what might have become of me had I not had the transplant. I knew, meeting Michael and Pauline, that however bad this stage was, the alternative was much worse. At least I had hope on my side.

12. Life

Mid-October – December 2002

'COME ON GRANNY, come on.' The boy's shrill voice drifts down to me. I am standing, gasping and sweating, halfway up the awesome gradient of Wittenham Clumps, known locally as Mother Dunch's Buttocks. I have already been walking for two hours and now have to get to the top. I can just make out a curly blond head, waving and shouting, 'Granny, Granny, come on.'

'Who are you calling Granny?' I mutter to myself. 'Cheek.' I must look a bit granny-like, unfit, stopping every few steps, muscles aching. I set off again, slowly. 'Granny, come on, come on.' The voice is insistent. I throw my feet forward, pace by pace. In the side of my vision I make out a woman, rotund, in her sixties, ambling up the hill behind me. She is clearly finding it difficult, but keeps walking, smiling and waving to her grandson.

'Well, if Granny can do it, so can I,' I think to myself, setting out once more with steely determination. 'I'm not going to be beaten by Granny.'

Panting, I make it all the way to the top of the hill, giving the blond boy a big smile. He glances at me, indifferent, and turns back to cheering on Granny. At the top I don't stop. I keep going. Breathing hard, my legs groaning and finally adjusting to the idea that they have to move, I keep on walking. Round the top, the view of Oxfordshire spreading out below, golden in the mid-October sunshine, the Thames flowing under the bridge where the annual Poohsticks championships are held, Didcot Power Station in the distance. Down then up again to the top of an Iron-Age hill fort, where I finally stop and sit. I've done it. I've walked up a hill. And I am not exhausted, unable to walk another inch. I'm tired, but healthy tired, heart-pumping, life-giving sort of tired. I can keep going if I want to.

Mo and I sit in silence, contemplating what we've been able to do together.

'I've joined the human race, haven't I?' I eventually say.

'Yes, I think you have.' He takes my hand.

'And it is bloody hard work, isn't it?'

The whole thing had, so far, been bloody hard work and there was more to come. My last stay in Papworth had given me the strength to pick up and get on. I was still feeling nauseous and still being sick on occasions, but less so as the weeks passed. I was shaky and had some bad days when I could not see beyond my symptoms, but was beginning to experience more good days and a sense of being able to look towards my future. Having begun to feel a bit better in myself, life could begin in earnest. And that meant serious exercise.

Around three months, the breast bone heals completely and is strong enough to sustain normal weight once more. I could start ironing, lifting a tray, vacuuming, mowing the lawn, pouring a full kettle, doing press-ups – all these were now safe, without risk of splitting my sternum open. My cat, banned from sitting on my chest for three months, had learned to come up to me, pat my arm and retreat with a mournful look. At last I could invite her back to her favourite place, lying down the front of my body, paws stretched out, gazing deeply into my eyes, vibrating purrs and occasionally blinking to indicate her pleasure. The cat was back, my chest was healed, but after years of inactivity I had no muscles. My arms had shrunk to little sticks on the end of my shoulders. When I tried a bit of ironing, my arms hurt and trembled like jelly. It was time for the gym.

I had joined a health club several years earlier, rather optimistically in the circumstances. I had been in the gym once or twice – taking the lift up to the first floor, unable to manage the stairs – and had a go on the treadmill, setting it to a slow walking pace. I had felt rather conspicuous amongst the gleaming muscled gods and goddesses of North Oxford, pumping and strutting their stuff, and retreated to the safety of the slow lane in the swimming-pool. Now, however, was time for pumping and strutting myself.

The thought of going to my health club again filled me with a mixture of excitement and terror. I'd managed at the hospital gym and had been going for walks for a few weeks, religiously doing my exercises, but knew that real gyms, for normal people, were in a different league. The machines were something else, with no super-low settings for the newly transplanted. I knew I was still a weakling, the weak one. I, with my fat, hairy face and spindly arms, would be in the midst of the pink people, trying to look like one of them. I took the plunge and phoned up to renew my membership. Accompanied by Mo, a bag to be sick into if necessary and a large amount of trepidation, I climbed the stairs at the health club and walked into the gym.

Matt, a twenty-something ball-of-muscle fitness instructor, sits me down to devise a plan. He is initially hesitant about taking on such a case as mine, then enthusiastic at venturing into new territory. 'You'll be great for my CV,' he tells me. I explain what I'd learned from the physiotherapists at Papworth.

'My heart and lungs have not got their own nerve supply and my heart will only speed up when it gets the right signals from my muscles,' I tell Matt. 'And I won't necessarily start breathing more when I need to because my lungs won't recognise the fact that I am exercising.'

Matt raises his eyebrows. 'Wow. So you can't use heart rate as a measure of fitness?'

I nod.

He deletes the information about heart rate from my computer records, saying, 'We won't need all that.'

I explain how I need to wait for the catecholamines from my

muscles to get the new organs into gear.

Matt talks fast, clicking the computer. 'You need to build up gradually over time. One step at a time, not all at once. Each time, warm up, stretch, do the workout, then cool down. Stretch, then chill out.'

It sounds exhausting. I sit in his office feeling sick, my legs shaking even before I'd tried anything. Matt leaps up. 'Right, let's go, let's get you started.'

I trail after him across the gym, trying not to knock into the intimidating machinery. He stops at an exercise bicycle, nothing like Papworth's: all flashing lights and multiple programmes.

'I suggest you start with ten minutes warm up on the bike,' Matt says, patting the seat invitingly. 'You can set it to different levels. I've programmed in level three to start with, very easy, very gentle. Just pedal slowly and speed up once you start to feel warm.'

I climb on the bike, nearly falling off trying to get my feet in the pedals. I push down on one side. Nothing happens.

'Just push. Start pedalling,' Matt encourages me.

'I am pushing,' I reply. Slowly the pedal moves down and then stops again. I push and push and can just about get it round one revolution before stopping, gasping. I want to lie down on the floor and sob. I am transported back to being a small child at school, an impossibly complicated mathematical equation in front of me with no idea how to do it. I want to run away and never try again. I remember the smug pronouncements of my teacher when I was seven: 'Diana could be good, but she gives up too easily.'

'I think the level is too high,' Matt says. 'Let's try again – Level two should be fine.' It wasn't, neither was level one. I manage about thirty seconds of severe, mind-over-matter effort, my legs crying out in pain.

'I think we need to rethink this a bit,' Matt concludes. He skips off into the office, taps at the computer and returns. 'Okay, we'll start with the treadmill and with a bit more body conditioning to get those muscles woken up.'

And so the treadmill it was, initially five minutes at a slow pace, gradually speeding up to a normal walking pace then a bit brisker. And I sat on strange contraptions, lifting my legs, up, down, pushing my shoulders and arms against five kilogram weights, imagining my muscles growing, responding, strengthening. Waking up.

Now, three years later, my gym work consists of ten minutes on an exercise bike at level four to warm up, then twenty minutes fast walking and jogging on the treadmill or twenty minutes on a cross-trainer and a circuit of weight machines. Or a long lie-in feeling guilty. Now, I have the language, too and the gear – lycra tops, different shoes for cross-training and jogging, earphones to listen to the TV to stave off boredom. But then, I arrived in the gym in a pair of baggy joggers and tee shirt and wanted to blend into the background. Everyone else seemed to know what they were doing. I felt an outsider, an intruder on the world of the fit. But one of them I could and would, become.

To pass the time and take my mind off my exertions, I chatted to anyone who would listen. I talked to one young woman lifting weights next to me.

'How often do you do this?' I asked her.

'Every day,' she replied.

'Wow. You must be fit,' I said.

'Actually, I'm trying to make out,' she whispered, giggling. 'See that guy over there, the blond one? No no, don't look now.'

I peeked surreptitiously at the nice young men pumping iron, who all looked the same to me.

'Isn't he a babe?' she said. 'I'm just trying to find out when he's here – Monday and Wednesday for definite.' I wished her good luck. Later, delighted, she told me she had a date. I never saw her again after that.

Before the transplant, I looked at what I deemed to be normal, fit people and thought it was easy for them to walk fast, run, cycle. If not easy, a matter of simple persistence. Enviously I watched people running along chatting, and thought it looked effortless. I watched dancers moving with grace and ease across the stage, leaping, twisting, bending, and thought it was painless. I thought it was all easy for those who were able to breathe. If and when I had a normal heart, then these things would become possible. Just a matter of a bit of hard work, patience and practice, and I too would be up and running.

The classic TV programme 'Candid Camera' once set up a spoof machine where women could lie down on a conveyor-belt one end, go through a tube and come out the other end a few moments later fully made up, manicured, coiffured and beautified. A surprising number of women, completely taken in, signed up to buy one. During my exertions at the gym, I often longed for a machine I could just get into and emerge from the other end with rippling muscles, stamina and legs like those of a long-distance runner. After years of inactivity and a lifetime of not being able to run, my muscles had no memory of what movement was all about, no core strength to fall back on. I had no role-models to follow. I put the time in, and while I could obviously do more than was possible before the operation, the fitness I associated with having a whole heart was not easy or swift to achieve. That wasn't to be.

I turned up at the gym day after day, and many times I felt reduced to tears. Many times I did not want to go, feeling nauseous, sick, uncomfortable, tired, but I forced myself. My muscles hurt, I seemed to be miles behind everyone else, the exercise would make me feel sick. I wanted to escape from it all, and occasionally thought longingly of the days when I could just sit in my wheelchair and not have to make all this effort. But somehow I kept going. 'Just do it, just do it,' I said over and over again. Mo came to the gym with me in those early days. He was not particularly keen, preferring to get his exercise chopping down trees, walking or cycling, but he was there with me, sweating it out.

Gradually, slowly, the computerised machines clocked up my progress. I moved from five minutes slow walking to seven minutes, ten minutes. Then slightly faster, and faster again, until one day I suddenly started to feel hot, with sweat breaking out down my back, my heart thumping in my chest. I couldn't see Mo, he was busy on the rowing-machine. I was on my own, dying.

Panicked, I got off the treadmill and walked slowly to Matt in his office.

'Something's happening. I don't feel very well,' I told him.

He sat me down and asked me to describe my symptoms.

'I was on the treadmill, going quite fast, faster than yesterday and I felt really hot, sweaty, I could feel my heart hammering in my chest …'

Matt started smiling, jumped up and nearly pushed me out of the door. 'This is great,' he said. 'Your muscles are catching up, you're ready to go. This is just normal, what happens – you're warming up, your heart is going faster – you're getting fit.' I got back on the treadmill, terrified and kept going. I walked, marched fast, until my face glowed, I was damp with sweat and my heart felt like a battering-ram inside me. I was breathing heavily, but not gasping for breath like I used to.

I had lived all my life according to one set of rules, which told me that getting out of breath was dangerous. I had learned to spot the early signs and slow down or stop, to take life easy. Now I simply did not know what to expect, what was normal. I was told that I had to exercise until I was slightly out of breath and then keep going. Becoming hot and sweaty, and setting my heart pumping, was healthy, not a sign of imminent collapse. Each time I did this, my mind screamed 'Stop!' but my forty-six-year-old alarm had to be overridden. I had a lot of learning to do.

The gym ran a regular sequence of competitions to keep us motivated. One was to tot up the equivalent of a journey from Lands End to John O'Groats on the exercise machines, each minute counting as a mile. I entered the competitions, determined to aim if not for the bottom then one or two from the end. By the time the other, fit, participants had completed their metaphorical journeys across the country, I had just reached the Devon–Cornwall border, but was pleased to see one person behind me, stuck at St Ives.

Life became a series of firsts. The first time I walked to the end of the road to post a letter. The first time I went into town, alone. The first time I went out in the evening. My first dance. My first hill, my first trip on a train. My first swim with my new heart and lungs, finding that I could hold my breath and swim underwater, swim a whole length without gasping, then twenty more. I drove the car for the first time for twenty months, practising around an empty supermarket car park one Sunday evening, apprehensive at first but finding it all came back within minutes. Then my first drive around the roads, finding that the traffic had increased and got much faster since I'd last driven. The first time on a bicycle, wobbling at first then taking off, true to the adage that one never forgets. My first supermarket shop, managing to carry all the bags into the house by myself. The first time I had tea in Jacky's garden and lifted two-year-old Julian, swinging him up in the air, both of us shrieking with delight.

Everything I did those first few months was accompanied by the noise of the medication. The side-effects rose and fell in sequences, as though they were playing a chemical version of Ravel's 'Bolero'. Nausea was the first player, moving in louder and louder until it dominated. Then shaking, starting with a faint tremor in the fingers, moving down to the whole hand, rendering handwriting useless, causing tea to spill and culminating in myoclonic twitches making me jump. Then constant fullness in my stomach, churning, gurgling, unable to empty its contents except for upwards. Moving on now to headaches, starting slowly with a twinge above the right eye, spreading over the face, down into the teeth and neck until all that can be heard is pain. Tightness in my chest, my breathing tearing against scar tissue, wrenching, searing in the morning, subsiding to a dull ache by the end of the day. All these reared up, then receded, reared up and receded like repetitions of the 'Bolero'. I thought I had heard the last of one, only for it to call out again a week, two weeks later.

I learned to listen and observe the side-effects, to let them wash over me without trying to play them or alter the music. I learned that they all had a voice that needed to be expressed and once sounded, became distant. I learned to watch mindfully and wait. Not panic, rush off to try and do something – take another drug, stop the medication, seek medical advice – but watch, observe quietly. I had started a form of meditation called Mindfulness while on the waiting-list. In the past, I'd never got on very well with meditation. I had tried, thinking it would be good for me, but my busy brain rushing on to the next thing then the next, and the speed at which I felt I had to lead my life, always made me stop after just a few attempts.

However, now that I had time on my hands and a strong need to live in the present, it seemed to make more sense. I read a book on Mindfulness, *Full Catastrophe Living* by Jon Kabat-Zinn, written in common-sense language, giving simple ideas about living now rather than in the past or future, observing what is going on rather than always reacting, allowing things to change on their own rather than constant push, push. It made sense and I started with the help of tapes to guide me. I was neither thorough nor religious about it but found that it always helped. By observing, rather than reacting to, even strong physical sensations of pain, nausea or shaking, these seemed to become more manageable, would metamorphose into something else, seem more distant. I learned to live more firmly in the present.

My body learned to accept the drugs and let them do their work without making a fuss. The shaking subsided into a slight tremor in my hands, which eventually disappeared when I changed the immunosuppressant medication for the third time. The nausea gradually diminished and stopped, and my stomach eventually settled. All the discomfort and churning, I was told, were caused by damage to the gastric nerve during surgery, which affected how my stomach emptied itself. Miraculously, the nerves sorted themselves out within a few months, allowing my digestive system to work properly again. Confusion, forgetfulness, bursts of energy followed by sluggishness, dissociation, feeling unreal, inability to concentrate – these came and went.

Gradually, too, my heart and lungs settled in and began to feel ordinary, normal. For a few months after the operation, my new organs did not feel like mine. Part of someone else was living inside me, alien – not unwanted, but not familiar. One Sunday afternoon, I was lying on the bed trying to rest. I was just drifting into sleep, my mind roving over a nonsense of dreams, when I woke with a start. Someone was hammering, on and on, down the road. Bang, bang, bang.

'It's Sunday. Who on earth is doing their DIY on Sunday?' I muttered to myself. I tried to block out the sound, then went to the window to see who was making the noise. Bang bang bang. On and on. I lay down again. Mo must have heard my mutterings, and came into the bedroom.

'Is that Anthony?' I asked him. 'Can you tell him to stop for an hour or so while I rest?'

'What noise?' Mo said. 'I can't hear anything.' He went to the window and looked out. 'No, all quiet.'

'But can't you hear it?' I lay down, bemused, annoyed. I tapped out the rhythm on the bedside table. Bang bang bang. Mo lay down next to me and took my wrist. 'Bang, bang, bang,' he said, in time to my pulse.

'That's it, my heart-beat.' I could hear it, I could not get it out of my head. My new heart-beat transmitted through my tissues to the tiny bones in the ear – the malleus, incus and stapes – on to my inner ear to the auditory nerve, picked up as foreign, unfamiliar and therefore amplified.

'Can you hear your own heart beating?' I asked Mo.

'No,' he told me, 'but it's not so new as yours.' I tried to rest, but my mind was continually drawn to the insistent heart-beat, enquiring, 'What is this, what is this, what is this?' with each pulse.

My brain needed several weeks to accept the new noise as normal and to screen it out in the way those living near busy roads eventually cease to hear the traffic. These days, I can't hear it if I try. But back then, the drum-beat accompanied me throughout the day, perking up in moments of quiet and coming into its own at night. I learned to listen for a while then move my mind on. It's okay, I told myself. Nothing to be frightened of. This is my new friend. Get used to it. It's here for life. And eventually my brain got the message.

*   *   *

It took about four months for me to realise that I was alive, that I had been through a heart and lung transplant and was now out the other side. My father had asked me, when I came home after the transplant, whether I was aware of waking up after the surgery and saying to myself, 'Thank goodness – I'm alive.' I had no memory of that. The first few months were so much concerned with getting by, moment by moment, struggling through the thick treacle of surgery and drug side-effects, that I did not have a chance to be aware, really aware, of what I'd been through. I had to get used to the drugs and try and regain some strength: any awareness of the bigger issues of life and death had to be put to one side.

One afternoon at the end of October, I sat in my office sorting through paperwork: paying bills, writing letters and emails, chucking out junk mail. Writing to people who had sent me flowers and presents in hospital. Such ordinary tasks had been beyond me for several weeks. Writing a simple note, signing my name, required absorbed concentration because my hands shook so much. I look back on things I wrote in my diary those days and can hardly make out the words. But here I was, the last of the day's sunshine filtering through the window, getting on with some routine tasks. I started doodling a picture of my life on the back of a bank statement. A long blue line, moving downward, turning thin and bleak towards the end of the last forty-six years; then a big black dollop, the operation and the months to follow, black scribbles, overlaid with purple zigzags and yellow panic; then finally, a turquoise-white line leading out of the mess, leading upwards. Here I was now, moving away from the mess of the last few months and it was all over. I had a new heart and lungs and my new life was ready to begin. A large penny dropped that afternoon. I could at last say to myself, 'I've done it. The transplant is over. I am alive.'

I am alive, yes, but my donor, the person who made it all possible, is not. My life was at someone else's expense. During the months since the operation I had been aware of my donor, thinking about her, but somehow not really being able to take it all in. My donor had died and given me new organs, but I could not digest and absorb the information. Finally, during the autumn of 2002, I began to reflect on it all and realise the enormity of what had happened both for myself and for my donor. I was able to begin to make sense of living with the heart and lungs of someone who had died.

During the final few months of waiting for the transplant I had convinced myself that I would eventually get the organs of a young man, perhaps in his late teens or early twenties. I don't know why I thought this, or whether everyone waiting forms an image of who their donor might be, but this was what I imagined. It seemed unbearably painful to think of a family losing such a young person, suddenly, tragically and I could never think about it for too long. A few days after the operation, sitting on my bed in Mallard Ward, I finally asked Helen about my donor, frightened that she would confirm what I believed.

'Your donor was a thirty-one-year-old woman,' she told me, gently. 'She died very suddenly of a brain haemorrhage. She would not have known anything about it.'

I sat quietly with this information. It was too much to think about just then, when I had to struggle through the mists of surgery, anaesthesia and medication, struggle my way out of hospital and begin the long recovery. The information sat there in my mind, needing to be examined at some time, but not just then. It really came to me when I started going to the gym, surrounded by women in their early thirties, and tried to imagine what life was like for them. Thirty-one seemed a terrible time to die.

I formed a transient picture of my donor in my mind, which vanished and re-formed then melted again. But she was there, one way or another. I felt sure that my donor was very fit, perhaps exercised regularly, perhaps went running. I wondered about her – did she have children? Was she popular? How many people are affected by her death? I imagined her funeral and what I would have said if I was there. I wanted to thank her for what she had done for me. At some stage in her life, she had picked up an organ donation card, signed it and put it in the post to be registered. She had ticked a box saying 'I request that after my death my kidneys/corneas/heart/lungs/liver/pancreas be used for transplantation.' She carried a card proclaiming, 'I would like to help someone to live after my death.' I wondered if, when she had signed the card, put it in her purse or bag or left it at the back of a drawer, she had any idea that one day, well before her time, she would give part of herself to someone she did not know. What a deeply generous thing to do.

Many people have asked me if I feel different now, whether I have become my donor in any way. 'Does it change you?' they ask, 'having someone else's organs inside you?' Before the operation, I'd watched an American television programme about a group of transplant patients who felt that they had taken on the characteristics of their donors. In 1988, Claire Sylvia received the heart of an eighteen-year-old man who had died in a motorcycle accident. Soon after the operation Claire noticed that her tastes and attitudes began to change. She started to crave beer, which she had hated before, and described herself as acting 'more masculine'. She began having recurring dreams about a man named Tim L. When she met those whom she describes as the 'family of her heart', Claire discovered that her donor's name was, in fact, Tim L. and that all the changes she had been experiencing closely mirrored Tim's preferences and attitudes.

The phenomenon experienced by Claire has been reported a number of times. Some people report foreign memories, strange new personal preferences or new talents. In one grisly tale, a child received the heart of a ten-year-old girl who had been murdered in a crime that was unsolved. The eight-year-old recipient then began to experience recurrent nightmares about the man who had murdered her donor. She, her mother and her psychiatrist were so convinced that the dreams were true, that they reported her experiences to the police. On investigation the dreams were found to be accurate in terms of the identity of the murderer and the murder weapon, place and even the murderer's clothes.

Roald Dahl, in his book *Kiss Kiss*, tells a story about a woman whose husband was very abusive to her. When he died, the woman took her revenge by keeping one of his eyes alive in a goldfish bowl in order to make spiteful comments to it whenever she passed. All the beleaguered husband could do was to narrow his pupil. The story implies that somehow the husband's soul remained in his eye tissues, eternally subject to his wife's timely revenge, but unable to retaliate. In the cases of organ donation, these stories imply that the personality of the donor resides in the organs in cellular memory, and that the soul of the donor is carried into the recipient through implanted tissues, to exert its influence for ever.

For me, I cannot say that I noticed any changes other than those that could be explained by my experience of major surgery and the medication. I am still most definitely me, only more alive, more energetic and louder. That is not to say I was unaware of my donor. I thought about her most days, as though followed by a presence. I did not feel spooked or obsessed. Just a quiet reminder, a need out of respect to remember, to whisper a word of thanks to her. Thanks when I reached the top of my first hill, when I could manage half an hour cycling in the gym. Thanks when I first walked five miles, when I saw my friend's newborn twins for the first time. And thanks, tinged with sadness, over Christmas 2002, when I sat with all my family warmly replete with food and wine, laughing at an old family joke. I looked round at them all and thought that this would have been a very different occasion if it was not for someone we had never met.

13. Me, Me, Me

January–June 2003

A FEW YEARS AGO, when I was struggling to balance my work as a psychologist with my deteriorating health, I saw a patient who told me he wanted to kill himself. I thought I was understanding. I thought I said the right thing, but was drawn up short by a letter of complaint, saying that I was not at all sympathetic, even dismissive. I thought long and hard about the letter. Part of me wanted to deny it, to say I was doing my best; another part of me wanted to hang my head in shame and give up, never see patients again. But on reflection I knew that that person had hit a nerve in me, as I had in him: who was he, healthy, fit, to want to chuck his life away when I was struggling to keep on with mine?

I now know what it feels like to fall to the depths and not be able to see a way back, to meet terror face to face. I may now have more of an idea of what my patient was going through, and would hate to have been on the receiving end of what I inadvertently dished out. I know I did not always cope well with the transplant, and at times did not cope at all. I'd certainly looked down to the bottom, contemplated my death. But once I started to feel better, once the scars began to heal, the drugs settled down, my muscles developed, I was about to lead my life in a completely new way. I was now facing up to the challenge of being alive.

My first year of life with my new heart and lungs was like having my early years all over again, metamorphosing from a toddler to a

139

teenager, everything changing minute by minute. Only this time, anything was possible. No more breathlessness, no limitations. During the year after the transplant, I still got bad days, incapacitated by headaches or vague malaise I attributed to the medication. But on good days, the world became full of exciting possibilities.

Mo and I walked like maniacs, carrying picnics and waterproof clothes, on great adventures where I could explore what I was capable of. We walked in Oxfordshire, Devon, Cornwall, Scotland. We walked in the Black Mountains, and later in Switzerland. We spotted birds and flowers, walked in the frost and snow and rain. One year after the transplant, Mo and I walked for eight miles through London – the longest I had walked for many years – on a sponsored walk for the Grown-Up Congenital Hearts patients' association. I also had my first attempt at running. When I was on the waiting-list for the transplant, I dreamed of running across fields and moors, taking off and swooping over the sea, watching tiny islands below. In my dreams it was easy, effortless to run a marathon, a one-minute mile. In reality, that first run around the park, with my sister Chris, a marathon-runner, to encourage me, was excruciating – my legs hurt, I gasped for breath and became hot, beetroot-red and sweaty. But it was my first run, my first ever proper run.

What gave me great satisfaction was being able to do the ordinary routine things of life. I could now use a vacuum cleaner, which had been impossible for years. Once my appetite came back, I started to cook and found I could lift a casserole into the oven without struggling and gasping. I could bend down to pick up something off the floor and not get stuck there. I could do the gardening, mow the lawn. Put out the rubbish, lift a load of shopping. What pleasure could be gained from cleaning the toilet!

Now I could do things, I wanted to try everything. I drew the line at some activities. Bungee-jumping and parachuting were not at the top of my list, due to my terror of heights. But I tried out all the classes at the gym – body-conditioning; aerobics; legs, bums and tums; modern dance – most of which were aimed at the fit twenties.

I hid at the back of the class doing my own thing, trying to keep up. I had a go at salsa dancing, ceroc and jive, gyrating wildly and with unnecessary vigour just because I could. I narrowly avoiding breaking Mo's nose in an over-enthusiastic spin, sending his glasses crashing to the floor. I danced around the kitchen, leaped around when cleaning the house, and occasionally broke into a cha-cha-cha in the street. I wanted to talk non-stop. My voice took a few weeks to return fully following slight damage from the ventilation tube in intensive care. By the time it came back, thoughts and ideas were bubbling up inside me and I wanted to share my excitement with the world. I watched, amazed, as a constant stream of words flowed out of my mouth, hardly stopping for breath. When I saw friends, family, I wouldn't stop talking, pinning them to the wall with a torrent of words.

'Nobody,' my father commented, 'can get a word in edgeways. We used to be able to have a conversation. Now, you conduct a conversation.'

I wanted to conduct everyone's life as well. With my new-found energy and enthusiasm, I could help other people, and instead of always having to ask for assistance, could now offer my muscles to others. Throughout my illness and recovery, my parents had started being my mother and father again after years of our relationship being on a more adult footing. They brought round casseroles, vats of soup, would drive me around, do the ironing, pick up prescriptions. They rallied to the cause. But now I could put my relationship with them back in its rightful place. Not that they always wanted my help, submitting with a laugh or gasp of wonder as I'd heave bags of shopping into the house, shift furniture or carry laden trays, give them long lectures about what they should be doing, how they should lead their lives. My mother wanted, as always, to tell me to slow down, but would laughingly accept my efforts. One Sunday morning we chatted on the phone about our plans for the day.

'Please,' she said to me, 'don't go for one of your long walks or cycle rides.'

'Why not?' I queried.

'Because you make me feel tired,' she replied.

My mother was not the only person I was making feel tired. My high spirits and energy seemed endless. I wanted to catch up, do everything I could now that I was able to, make up for lost time. Now I can do it, I not only would but should. As though I had a right to do anything I wanted to. My enthusiasm made me blind to others, not wanting to have to accommodate their needs for fear of missing out. I was being, in short, a selfish cow.

One evening, Mo and I went to our salsa class, then on to a bar. We went in, the room full of swaying couples moving to the Latin beat. Mo went to get a drink and one of our classmates asked me to dance. I went and had a go, spinning and wiggling and shrieking with laughter. The dance ended, another man grabbed my hand and we were off again. What fun. I could do this all night. I saw Mo and staggered over, catching my balance after repeated rotations and put my arm around him.

'Come on, let's dance,' I shouted, pulling him towards the dance-floor.

'No, I want to go now,' he said, grabbing his jacket and walking towards the door.

We left. I was silenced.

'I thought we were going to dance together,' he said. I tried to remonstrate, explain. He interrupted me. 'This is the first time we've had a chance to dance together and look what happens. It's always about your needs these days, isn't it? Not mine, not ours. Yours.'

We walked back to the car, Mo for once walking faster than me. I did not know what to say. What on earth was going on? What had I done? Mo was clearly deeply hurt but I didn't understand, then. We tried to talk as we drove back.

'I'm sorry,' I said. 'I didn't mean to hurt you, I was just having fun,' then tailed off into silence, listening to myself. Me, me, me.

When we got back, we tried to talk. We stood in the kitchen, the cats curling round our legs hoping we might have forgotten that we had fed them earlier. We both knew we'd hit something important, words could not be taken back, but we did not know where to go from there. 'I'm sorry,' Mo said. 'I just can't talk about this at the moment.' That night we retreated to opposite sides of the bed, rather than sleeping curled and spooned into each others' bodies. The next day, after a sleepless night, Mo left early for work. I'd arranged to go for a walk with my friend Elaine that morning, and as we climbed up the hill to Wytham Woods, explained to her what had happened.

'You know, he's quite right,' she said. 'Think of Mo. He's put all this time in, he's been looking after you, watching you go through that awful operation, been with you all the time. And what does he get now? You're like a bull in a china-shop, you never stop, he can't keep up.'

I listened, humbled.

'None of us can keep up,' she went on. 'We're all getting older. We're feeling our age. We can't keep up with you. You're making us all feel ancient. It is completely exhausting. Now, you're like a, like a …' She struggled for the words.

'Deranged teenager?' I offered.

'Yes that's exactly it. You're like a deranged teenager.'

I wanted to blame who I'd become on something else, my drugs, my donor. It must be the steroids, I told myself. I think partly that was true. I had experienced the depression they can cause and now had a dose of the other side, feeling manic, speedy, full of life, wanting to run and jump and hop and shout all at the same time. People were in general tolerant, would join in my high spirits, but not always. I'd been given a huge amount from other people, especially Mo and my mother, and I was not really giving much back. Throughout my illness and recovery, I had been the centre of attention, got support and help from others, had their love and concern. Mo had chosen to deal with it all in a different way, getting on with whatever needed to be done, quietly coping while inside facing his own struggles.

That evening and over the weeks and months to follow, Mo and I began to talk about what he'd been through. He began to be able to tell me what it had been like for him, watching me go through the operation, struggling to recover.

'I was terrified at times,' he told me. It was so obvious but yet he'd never said it, until then. He'd coped and coped, kept his head down and kept on. He'd always tried to be optimistic, to do what needed to be done to get my life and our lives together back on track. He'd felt helpless at times.

'All the time you were waiting, I'd been able to help, do things for you,' he said. 'When I watched you go into the operating theatre, there was nothing I could do, nothing. It was over to other people.' He stopped, choked by the memory of waiting to be told whether I'd survived the operation. 'Now, you're off doing your own thing and I sometimes wonder if you need me anymore.'

'Of course I do,' I said, crying with him. 'Of course. I couldn't have done any of this without you. You made it all possible, you've done the whole thing with me.'

We'd made our vows to stay together in sickness and in health and we had certainly had the sickness, the bad times. Mo had managed alone, in his own way. Our friends had offered to help but he had shut down and coped on his own. Whatever I threw at him, the illness, my despair and rage, he'd dealt with, but at what cost to him? In many ways, my life had become his life. He was willing and able to do that for me, believing that things would get better, but he'd given up so much in the process. What Mo had done was remarkable, amazing, and am I not sure that, had our roles been reversed, I would have had the kind of personality and deep confidence to be able to do the same for him. I had got most of the attention but it was Mo's transplant as much as mine. He deserved an Oscar, a standing ovation, for what he had done.

And now we had the health, the good times. So much is written and spoken about how couples manage during times of adversity. The stresses and strains on the carer, the need for him or her to get support as well. And then what happens when it all changes, when the cared for no longer needs the carer in the same way? When the dynamics have to change?

In our case, we somehow got on with adjusting and adapting. Mo's life had been put on hold because of my illness and suddenly, we realised, there was a big hole and he wasn't in the right place for him. He had originally trained as an environmentalist and this was the work he loved. When I became ill, he took more certain and better-paid work in computing, which he did not particularly like but which enabled us to be financially secure. Now, with his full-time job as carer coming to an end, he had the chance to look again at what he wanted. We talked, we planned and thought about him for a change. What Mo needed and wanted, what was important for him.

My family, too, were no doubt affected by the changed dynamics. Like many families we do not speak openly of our particular roles or how we get on together, but from seeing a lot of my parents, needing their help, needing them as parents once again, we had to negotiate the changes in our relationship. I realised I had flown away with little thanks and needed to take more care, to think more of others, give a bit more.

I took a long, hard look at my new life during the weeks and months after the row between Mo and me, which we came to realise was a turning-point for both of us. I began to think, seriously, what I was going to do with this new life of mine. All this going to the gym and going for walks was all very well, but life was getting too comfortable. Hedonistic, even. Mo gave me a little present as a joke, a silver dice to help me decide what to do each day. Throw it and my day would be determined. The dice came in a pink box with the title 'Ladies who Lunch'. My choice for the day was cocktails, shopping, hairdo, gym, detox or lunch.

That little silver dice spoke volumes to me. My donor had passed on her life to me and what was I going to do with that life? Hone my skills as a lady who lunches? It had been fine for a while but I had to find some kind of purpose. I needed to get back to work.

Work had always been so important to me. Not only that, but I'd trained as a psychologist and cognitive therapist and it seemed such a waste not to use what I was capable of, to put something back in the world. My first step was to go to a conference in May, nearly one year after the transplant. I walked into the hotel in Stratford, carrying my bag, and spotted an old colleague whom I had not seen for ages. I smiled and waved at him and started to walk over. He looked at me in shock, dropping his files on the floor, exclaiming, 'Diana, I thought you were dead!' Word had got out amongst psychology circles that I was having a transplant, but the gossip had not got around to the rest of the story, so I was, officially, deceased.

'No, I'm not dead yet,' I replied. 'Nice to see you too.'

Now that I was officially alive, I turned up at social events organised by my work, made contact with my colleagues, and contributed to a book with members of Oxford's psychology department. After the quiet of life at home, being a patient for such a long time, I felt overwhelmed by all these people. To begin with, I was treated as a minor celebrity. People I'd not got on with or rubbed up against at work gave me their best wishes, were even nice to me. 'Diana,' they would exclaim, 'how are you? I heard you were ill …'

I was amazed by how many people knew about my operation. From keeping my health a closely guarded secret, it was now out in the open, common knowledge. And for once, I no longer minded. My half a heart was history, I had new apparatus with, admittedly, a new set of problems, but these could be discussed and shared. I felt, in fact, almost a duty to tell people what I'd been through, in the hope that they too would stop and think about organ donation, perhaps tell a friend, family member, that they knew someone who had a transplant, perhaps, at last, get round to registering as a donor.

I needed to re-train to check that I was up to date as a psychologist. To begin with, I was terrified. My brain felt like cotton-wool, unable to shape itself around anything more complicated than gossip or working out a shopping-list. I sat in lecture rooms making myself ask questions or make comments to test out whether I still had a mind or not. Gradually I remembered what I knew, learned some more and was ready to be let loose on the public. I started seeing patients. Mindful of the mistakes I'd made in the past, mindful of what the past years had taught me, I sat in the therapist's chair and listened. As soon I started to work again, as soon as I sat down with my patients, I was gripped: absorbed in the story, absorbed in the person's plight. I remembered again the privilege to hear about the intricacies of people's lives, their thoughts and feelings. Sharing their secrets with me, a stranger. And knowing that, on perhaps a deeper level than before, I understood what it means to hit rock bottom.

*   *   *

At one year, we had a party to thank the many people who had helped us in so many ways. Recovering from the operation had been made possible by other people: friends, family, colleagues, professionals, neighbours, pharmacists, people who all gave me a hand. From the outside they could see our struggle, the enormity of what we'd been through and many chose to help out. To give me a bit of their wellness to keep me going. To help me laugh, notice how far I'd come rather than how far I still had to go. And to remind me that Diana was still in there, alive and kicking.

So a party it was, a celebration of life. A big party, a band, dancing, food, balloons. A posh frocks and varnished toenails sort of party. A one-year birthday cake. Tables with candles and confetti. The hall glowed as friends arrived. Jane and Roben from Scotland who'd phoned and visited; Amanda from Botswana keeping me going with her emails; Eleni who had come round to the house to teach Greek. My family and my parents' friends who had helped them get through the days while I was in hospital: Sidney, Jeannie and Charles, Gwyn and Joe. My niece and nephews, my sisters, my brother Rob. They poured in, some bringing presents, expressing their happiness for me. Brimming with hugs and smiles. I gave a speech to thank everyone and, at last, Mo got his standing ovation. That night we drank a toast to life, then friends and family proceeded to get legless and prance around to wild music, with decreasing grace and increasing gyrations, in the way that ageing hippies, children of the 1970s, have got down to a fine art. And all night I danced with Mo.

14. Becoming a Grown-Up
June 2006

IT IS NOW FOUR YEARS since my transplant. Life has been like a jigsaw puzzle thrown onto the table to be gradually reassembled. Now most of the pieces are in place, at least for the moment. Mo has a new job and has got his own life back on course. Papworth is celebrating twenty-five years of transplantation. My mother still tells me to take it easy, not overdo things: but these days, as she nears eighty, I give the same advice to her. I've settled into my new life and got used to living with different organs. My face is more or less as normal, allowing for the ravages of age and gravity. I'm back at work, where – to my relief – I am now treated as part of the furniture, as though I was never away. People moan at me without treating me as an invalid, and I knew my transplant journey was over when an old sparring-partner at work started to be rude to me again.

I still go to the gym, but not all the time as though my life depended on it. We've been back to New Zealand, where I walked the paths I'd struggled along with my old heart twenty-three years ago, amazed and delighted at the difference. My scars have healed, leaving a thin, 18-centimetre long slightly raised pink line down my front, four faint marks across my belly from the chest drains and a mark on my neck from the intravenous line. I do not try to hide the scars, but wear them with pride. Nobody seems to take much notice, although sometimes I get curious glances from people I don't know. The other day I went swimming with a friend's ten-year-old daughter. Sarah had a good look at my scar, felt it and pronounced 'Your scar is *weird*. But without it you'd be *dead*.'

She's right. Most days I remember the gift I've been given. I'll always be aware of my donor and often find myself wondering about her, thanking her for my life. Whenever I go into a church or cathedral, I light a candle for her and know that all my happy anniversaries and Christmases will be the opposite for her family.

Each day now I take about seventeen tablets at different times of the day, some with food, some without. Each morning when I wake up, I take my temperature, weigh myself and measure my lung function with a spirometer to check for any signs of infection or rejection, recording it all in my little blue book. I avoid eating shellfish or food that might be potentially dodgy, and try to avoid people who are blatantly infectious. I stay out of the sun, since the medication increases the risk of malignant melanomas amongst other cancers; when the sun comes out, so does my Factor 60 and a large white parasol. I try and put my feet up regularly to cope with my swollen ankles. This is all normal to me. Neither positive nor negative. Just what I do to keep well.

Life is not always easy and the transplant can and does cause problems which need to be managed. I have off days, when for some reason the side-effects of the medication, or residual exhaustion from the old days, weigh heavily on me. The immunosuppressants have already began to cause problems, my kidney function deteriorating more than it should have, which has to be checked regularly. I try not to think about the long-term implications, possible renal failure or a kidney transplant, more bridges to be crossed when and if I encounter them. Part of me is terrified, but a wiser part of me knows, with a quiet confidence, that whatever life throws at me, I'll somehow manage to deal with it, with the help of my long-suffering husband, family and friends. That is what I've learned most, the lesson I've gained from it all – the confidence that I can get through.

I've complete confidence in Papworth, too. At last my six-year-old sulky child has learned that the medics are on my side, that they are well worth listening to and that whatever problems arise from the transplant, they will do their best to resolve them. I remember John Dunning's words when I was put on the list for a transplant, hoping that the hospital staff feel like friends. If not friends, Papworth does feel like a sort of second home, or a familiar, friendly garage where I can take my problems and they'll be sorted out in a professional and skilful manner. I enjoy catching up with the gossip and going to see the ducks. Which is just as well, given how often I have to go there. Sometimes every few months, at the moment more often to sort out my renal problems. When I go, as an inpatient or outpatient, I'm warmly greeted as a friend. Whether or not this is done through clenched teeth as they remember my irritating habits of bringing a long list of queries and wanting to be in control of everything, with occasional helpful suggestions about how the service can be reorganised and improved, I do not know. If teeth are clenched, they hide it well.

I know I am one of the lucky ones. I've been given a chance. I'm alive when my donor is not. Like Pauline I might not be here at all. I think of the other people waiting for a transplant which may or may not happen. I think of Michael, who helped keep me going while I was waiting but only lived for three months after his transplant, and wish he'd had the same luck as me. Some people have a rougher ride in the first year than I did, facing more problems with acute rejection or ongoing infections. My donor was a very good match for me and I have not had any episodes of rejection and only a few, manageable infections. I am alive and well. Yes, I am very lucky.

Only a small proportion of the people who need a transplant will actually get one, the need for transplants always exceeding the number of organs available. According to statistics collected by UK Transplant, between 1st April 2005 and 31st March 2006, 2,795 organ transplants were carried out, from a total of 1,363 donors. The majority of transplants use organs from people who have died, the rest from live donors, such as in kidney transplants. Nearly 7,000 people in the UK are waiting for a transplant. Of these people, with current trends and statistics, it is likely that at least four hundred will die while waiting. For others, like Michael, by the time they have waited, their health will have deteriorated so much that surviving a transplant becomes difficult if not impossible.

The shortage of donors is always described as chronic, complex reasons dictating whether an individual or his or her family decide to donate organs in the event of a death. Culture, religion and ethnic group play a role. Most of the major religions in the UK support, in principle, organ donation and transplantation, while recognising that it is an individual choice. In many religions, the need to relieve suffering and save lives can override objections to interfering with an individual's body after death, but all cases are recognised as different. In Jewish law, for example, consultation with a competent rabbinic authority is required before consent can be granted. Originally the Muslim faith decreed that the body is sacred, chosen by God and therefore man cannot chose to desecrate it after death. In 1996 the Shariah Council, which decides Muslim law, issued a fatwa, a religious opinion, to support organ donation since it is a means of alleviating pain and suffering and saving lives. Now, theoretically, Muslims can carry donor cards, and a deceased individual's family can give permission for organs to be used to save another person's life. But it is not widely accepted, and there are some, minority, fundamentalist or extreme groups opposed to organ donation who will stick to the strict letter of the original doctrines.

Other religions are also accepting of organ donation, at least in principle. In Hindu scriptures there is the concept of *Daan,* or selfless giving. Hindus believe strongly in life after death, and things that promote and sustain life are acceptable. Sikh philosophy puts great emphasis on the importance of giving to others, putting others before oneself. Jehovah's Witnesses might be assumed to be against organ transplantation because of their objections to blood transfusions, but in fact they believe that donation is an individual decision and that transplantation is acceptable so long as blood is removed from organs or tissues before a transplant. Christian Scientists normally rely on spiritual rather than medical means of healing, but again view donation and transplantation as a matter for the individual.

Despite donation being, in theory, widely accepted, black and Asian people are heavily underrepresented on the organ donation register: only around 1 per cent of organ donors are Asian, and black people make up less than 0.5 per cent of donors. This is a significant problem in that black and Asian people are three to four times more likely than white people to need a kidney or heart transplant, due to a higher incidence of diabetes and heart disease. The success of kidney transplants in particular is greatly increased if the donor and recipient are from the same ethnic group.

Regardless of issues of culture and religion, far fewer people actually register to donate organs: only about a third of those who, when asked, say they agree to organ donation, have actually registered. An even greater proportion say that they have never discussed the subject or let their close relatives know of their wishes. If there is no evidence of an individual's willingness to donate – if there is no donor card or evidence of registration – and if the relatives are opposed, or cannot be found, then donation does not occur.

The UK currently operates an 'opt-in' policy, where the views of each individual and the relatives are taken into account. If someone has made clear his or her wishes to donate organs by registering or giving written instructions, then, legally, organs can be removed after death. However, the views of the relatives are also taken into account and can overrule the wishes of the deceased. Although their son, daughter, husband or wife may have had no objections to donating their organs, or even have registered, the family, unable to bear the idea of the loved relative's body going through any more trauma, may at the point of death decide not to allow the organs to be removed. Preserving a body intact at the point of cremation or burial may be, for some people, the only way they can show their deep love and respect for the lost person and enable them to grieve properly.

Some of the reasons why relatives do not give their consent to organ donation may be based on misunderstandings or myths. People have expressed concerns to me that registering as an organ donor would mean that the ventilator or life-support system may be switched off prematurely – the needs of the potential transplantee being seen as greater than the unfortunate person in intensive care. 'Maybe they wouldn't do everything possible to save me,' one friend commented. 'They'd say she could save loads of people with her organs. She might be a cabbage if she recovers, let's let her go.'

In fact, the process of collecting organs for donation is completely separate from the arranging of transplants. It is not as though the same doctor will be dealing with patients who may have conflicting interests – in one room, a patient who is dying, and in the other, a patient who needs a transplant – and must decide who lives and who dies. That would clearly mean doctors were playing God. It is not like that: it is all organised independently. A potential donor has to be certified brain dead by doctors who are independent of the transplant team before the subject of transplantation is even raised. Relatives' objections to the deceased's body being violated after death may not take into account that many deaths, particular in younger people, would need a post-mortem to establish cause, and the body would be 'violated' anyway.

Another reason that reduces the rate of organ donation is that, if a patient is in a critical condition, hospital staff are understandably reluctant to bring up the subject at a time when the relatives are already distraught. This problem is only just beginning to be addressed, with the employment specially trained staff in intensive care units, who know exactly how and when to discuss donation.

At a party last Christmas, I met a woman who told me that her son had died in an accident six months previously.

'He was fit, in the prime of life,' she told me, her voice thick with emotion. 'Everything worked fine. He was on a ventilator for three days. Three days I sat there, praying, praying. Then it was time to turn off the machine.' She paused and took my hand. 'We buried him. If he had helped other people, I know that would have been his wish and mine. It would have made it easier to know that people like you could carry on. But no one asked me.' We sat there in silence for a moment, people drinking and laughing around us.

'I'm so glad to meet you,' she said eventually. 'You've got your life ahead of you. And somewhere, a mother like me knows that her child has helped someone else.'

I have not met anyone who has agreed to have a relative's organs donated, so cannot speak for people in that position. But from what I have been told, relatives take comfort from the knowledge that the death was not totally in vain, or the complete end of that person. They take comfort from knowing that another person or several people are alive and well despite the death of their relative, baby or young child. I know that if anything were to happen to Mo and I was faced with losing him, both of us would want as much of possible of him to carry on in the form of his organs helping others.

Work is going on all the time to increase the donation rate through publicity campaigns and legislation. One solution is to implement an 'opt-out' or 'presumed consent' policy, where consent to donate organs is assumed unless the individual has expressed and registered otherwise. An opt-out system would assume that everyone has given their consent to organ donation unless they had opted-out in writing. Donation would be seen as the norm and relatives would not have to make such difficult decisions at the traumatic time surrounding a death. A pure opt-out system could even mean that the relative's views were not taken into account at all, or could be overruled. There are pros and cons to such a system. In countries adopting an opt-out system, such as Spain, Austria, Belgium and France, which have a higher rate of organ donation, it is not clear whether this system alone is responsible – Spain, with one of the highest rates of donation, has a higher rate of road-traffic accidents than the UK. Spain also operates a successful network of transplant coordinators in intensive-care units, coordinated by a central agency in Madrid. The coordinators identify potential donors by closely monitoring emergency departments and tactfully discussing the donation process with families of the deceased. In this way, fewer potential donors are missed. In Sweden, the donation rate is lower than the UK despite Sweden operating an opt-out system. Austria operates an opt-out system where the views of the relatives are not sought and can be overruled. People who have opted out, and who then need a transplant themselves, are placed at the end of the waiting-list.

Clearly an opt-out policy has its advantages, and while the supply of organs does not match the need, measures need to be taken to stop organs not being used when they could be. In the words of Christiaan Barnard, quoted in *Time* magazine in 1969, 'It is infinitely better to transplant a heart than to bury it to be devoured by worms.' But an opt-out policy could be a minefield where, say, an individual had expressed their objection to donation but not got around to registering to opt out and the organs are then removed, causing significant distress to the relatives. An opt-out policy takes no account of the meaning of donation to the recipient. I took a long time in accepting my new organs, knowing that someone else's heart was inside me, something else's lungs were doing my breathing for me. One day, though, my district nurse Celia reminded me, 'Your heart and lungs were a present. A gift. They are yours now.'

They seemed to bed in and settle down after that: and now, four years on, they are totally friendly and familiar. For me, too, I was able to write a letter to the family of my donor, to express my sadness for them and to thank them for what they had done for me. Knowing that my new heart and lungs were willingly given, with the consent of my donor and her family, was for me and for others an important part of the process of adjusting to my new life.

While so many people wait for a transplant, the question of money inevitably arises. I was surprised how many people asked me, when I was waiting for my transplant, why I did not seek private medicine. As though it was possible to bypass the shortage of organs with money. Unfortunately, at least in some parts of the world, it is. Recently a kidney was advertised for sale on the internet, leading to changes in federal law in America forbidding the sale of organs.

In the Philippines, a kidney can be sold for a couple of thousand dollars, tempting poor people to sell parts of their bodies in order to raise money for their families. It is also reported that some countries operating the death penalty remove the guilty parties' organs shortly after execution and then sell them on to the highest bidder. I hope I do not have to believe all the stories on the internet. Where money is involved, there is no end to the possibilities.

In the UK the debate continues, and changes in legislation are in the air. I guess the important thing for now is that everyone thinks about organ donation, talks about it and makes their wishes clear. Children, too, have their opinions. When I was on the waiting-list, I went on local television as part of a programme about organ donation. My sister Chris, a teacher, showed the programme to her class of thirteen-year-olds, as part of their current-affairs teaching. They were initially silenced, amazed that their teacher should have something so ordinary as a sister, then full of questions and fierce determination that I should be able to live and have a healthy life. I was enormously touched when Chris told me of their reaction, imagining a group of twenty noisy teenagers cheering me on. For these young people, so full of life and generosity, it is crystal-clear – if we have the opportunity to help others, then of course we do it. No question. But the issue is undoubtedly complicated and for now, those people currently waiting are part of the great transplant lottery.

There are developments being made all the time in alternatives to organ transplantation. Stephen Westaby in Oxford and others, are looking at the feasibility of left ventricular assist devices, mechanical hearts to help boost the left ventricle's pumping action. In November 2003, fifty-seven-year-old Jim Braid was the sixth person in the UK to receive a Jarvic 2000 permanent artificial heart, in a collaborative effort between the Royal Brompton and Oxford John Radcliffe hospitals. Ventricular assist devices were designed to help the patient stay alive while waiting for a transplant. But occasionally, once the device is implanted, the patient's own heart is able to rest and thereby recover sufficiently so that a transplant is no longer necessary.

Transplanting animal organs into humans, xenotransplantation, is another option, but so far such attempts have never been successful. The immune system is even better at detecting and fighting animal tissue than it is in rejecting foreign human tissue. All attempts at xenotransplantation, including transplants from primates, have failed. Work is going on at the moment in developing strains of pigs that are genetic hybrids with a small number of human genes, with the aim that the human immune system would not recognise these organs as foreign. However successful such scientific advances are, the ethical dilemmas cannot be easily overcome. There is considerable opposition to use of animals for transplantation, in the same way that there is in using animals for medical research.

One Saturday we cycled into town and parked our bicycles on Broad Street, near an animal-rights protest. I looked away from the posters of cats, dogs, rabbits being used for experimentation, drug testing, surgical practice. Twenty years ago I would have agreed with them: who are we to use and abuse animals, to treat them as lesser souls than us, in the service of mankind? It seemed so simple then. But on that Saturday, I scurried away and hid my head in shame. Without animal testing, I would not be there, cycling, breathing, living. I did not want to think how many animals had been used in the development of the medications I take each day to keep me alive, not to mention those used in testing the feasibility of transplants. I know that for me and no doubt for others, too, the idea of having an animal's organs inside me would be taking it all one step too far. I know that my donor made an active choice to allow her organs to be used after her death and that knowledge gives me comfort. I could not countenance the thought that some poor pig, after a miserable laboratory life, would be killed so that I could carry on. Ironic, since my life is so intimately connected with the use and abuse of animals, not only in the medications I take, but also in the fact that I eat meat, wear leather shoes and have no hesitation in sentencing slugs to death by drowning them in a bath of beer. I accidentally left my leather jacket in my bicycle basket when I went shopping that day and it was still there when I returned a few hours later. It was probably because of the huge police presence but maybe the animal rights protesters were practising what they preach, looking at my jacket in disdain.

Beyond the ethics of using animals in this way, there is the realistic chance that xenotransplantation could introduce new, deadly diseases into the human population. AIDS, for example, originated in primates, and it is thought that animals carry a number of diseases which are benign to them but would be fatal in humans. So by saving one individual by transplanting a pig or chimpanzee heart, we may inadvertently affect the health of the whole human population.

Growing tissues into viable organs is another option. Dame Julia Polak, the Professor of Endocrine Pathology at Imperial College, London, works on medical research into ways of repairing or replacing damaged or diseased human organs and tissues by tissue engineering and regeneration. This includes work on lung disorders and regeneration. In the midst of her work, Professor Polak found herself a sufferer of the very condition she was researching. She developed severe pulmonary hypertension and needed a heart and lung transplant. When she returned to work after the surgery, she gave an emotional lecture on lung disease, using her own lungs to illustrate the disease process of pulmonary hypertension.

In the long term, being able to grow new tissues and organs in the laboratory will hopefully begin to address the chronic shortage of donor organs that are available. Ideally, also, if new tissues can be grown from tissue originating from the recipient, then the problems of rejection can be overcome. So, too, can the medical problems caused by immunosuppressant medication. Imagine, if I had lived, say, fifty years in the future, as a child I would pop into hospital one afternoon for a quick biopsy of my heart and lung tissue. These are then passed to the tissue regeneration laboratory, where a three-dimensional organic 'scaffold' in heart and lung shapes are seeded with my cells. There they grow, over time, into an embryonic heart and lungs, which can then be placed into my body where they grow into functioning heart and lungs.

Transplants and their cost and effectiveness are by no means uncontroversial. The jury is still out as to whether heart transplants, for example, are worth the time and effort. Not only in terms of the operation, but also the cost of the immunosuppressant medication taken for life. I have never dared work out how much I cost the NHS when I go to the pharmacist every month to collect my medication. The pharmacists always give me a smile along with my large carrier bag, a friendly word, a genuine enquiry as to my health. They do not seem to mind how expensive I am. I wryly expressed my concerns to my GP who grinned at me and shot off, in a good impression of the L'Oréal Lady, 'Because you're worth it.'

Transplants are in many ways still in an experimental phase. Each one is new, introducing new methods and techniques. In 2000, a paper published in the *British Medical Journal* described how a group of 889 German patients fared with or without a transplant. The study concluded that transplants were only really effective, in terms of survival rates, for the very sickest patients. According to these criteria, I would not have had a transplant when I did and would probably not have recovered so well or so quickly. There were many criticisms of the study, including responses from Papworth, saying that the study took no account of quality of life, one of the major factors determining when and whether people opt for a transplant.

In order to determine whether transplants are truly effective and efficient treatments for the range of conditions they are used for, what is required is a randomised controlled trial. Half the patients, selected at random, would have a transplant and half would either wait longer or receive other forms of treatment. But so much is already known about transplants that such a trial could not and would not be ethically or morally feasible. Imagine if I had gone to Papworth to be put on the list and been handed an envelope, picked at random as if from a metaphorical hat, which determined whether I had a transplant or not. Imagine if the paper in the envelope had been blank, or said 'Sorry, better luck next time.' I think, personally, the proof is out there. A transplant is not an easy option. No one in their right mind would chose to go through such an experience unless they had to. No medic would choose a transplant for their patients over more conservative surgery or medical treatment. Transplants have a long way to go and will no doubt move a long way from where they are now in terms of surgical methods and medications, but there is little doubt that they do work for those that need them.

Many people, and many of those I have met in my hours sitting in the Transplant Continuing Care waiting-room at Papworth, are delighted to have been given a chance. John Fisher, who had a heart transplant in 2000 and set up a transplant website, has devoted his life to the cause of organ donation. He runs several marathons and half-marathons each year, completes sponsored bicycle rides and travels the length and breadth of the country on the organ donor bus to remind people to sign up. Jan, who had a heart transplant six years ago in Birmingham, found the whole experience very difficult and distressing: she broke her back shortly after the surgery due to the high doses of steroids making her bones brittle, and now she experiences continuing problems with medication side-effects, some of which have significantly affected her life. 'But think of what I've been through since then,' she told me. 'I've seen my first grandchild, I was around when my daughter did her GCSEs and A levels, seen Kate grow from a child into a teenager, I've had a wonderful fiftieth birthday party, celebrated twenty-five years of life with my husband and I've been to France, Spain and Italy and have had lots of brilliant times.' I've heard that story many times. It's the brilliant times, the stolen times, that count.

What am I going to do with this new life of mine? I am back at work, seeing patients, teaching, writing books. I like to think that I'm being of some use to other people. I am a wife, a daughter, a friend, an auntie. A regular patient at Papworth and quite a regular visitor to the GP. A bad-tempered cow on occasions – I'm impatient to fit it all in, stroppy when things go wrong, feeling that I am wasting my precious time. Most of the time I'm just getting on with the business of being alive. Like a blind person who then regains sight, I am still and hope always to be in awe of what I can now do – walk, laugh, do up my shoelaces, run up a flight of stairs, live my life. I hope never to take what I have got for granted. I know my new life is indeed a gift.

*   *   *

The other day I received a statement from the Pension Service telling me how much state pension I could expect to receive when I reach retirement age. They promised to pay me the princely sum of £83.97p a week for the rest of my life. For the first time in my life I realised that I may yet be alive to receive such a reward. Just maybe. I have met a woman who has lived for fifteen years with a heart, lung and kidney transplant. She had just returned from backpacking round Thailand and looked set for at least another fifteen years. Another woman who had a heart and lung transplant for cystic fibrosis twenty years ago and is still going strong, although now experiencing problems both from her original illness and from long-term effects of the medication. The survival rates are even better for heart transplants – Derrick Morris died after twenty-five years following one of the first heart transplants in the UK. These people are my role-models.

If I stay well, if I dodge all the infections buzzing around waiting to pounce on the immunosuppressed, if my body and new organs resist fighting with each other, if I am not killed by long-term side-effects of the medication, kidney failure, cancers, heart disease, lung disease, avoid getting run over, knocked off my bicycle or losing my way in the mountains in Scotland, and if I am not in the wrong place at the wrong time when a terrorist attack strikes, then maybe, just maybe, I'll yet become a pensioner. And all this serious thought about pensions and growing older made me realise that maybe this is it. Maybe, at long last, at the age of fifty, when I'm as old as my tongue, a little older than my teeth and fifteen years older than my heart and lungs, I've at last achieved my childhood ambition of becoming a grown-up.

When I told one of the doctors at Papworth that I was aiming for at least twenty years out of my transplant, he reacted with pursed lips and a sharp intake of breath in the way that builders do when asked about some impossibly complicated reconstruction, before saying 'It'll cost yer.' He gently reminded me of what might lie ahead, told me they could make no promises.

'But we'll do our best,' he said.

And so will I.

Acknowledgements

The fact that I am writing this book is thanks to the Transplant Unit at Papworth Hospital. I cannot describe what they have done for me without lapsing into the most appalling clichés. You've all been fantastic, particularly Helen Castle, Ann Thompson, and Celia Hyde and all the nurses in Transplant Outpatients. My great thanks to the doctors who have put up with my quest for knowledge and control – Dr Keith McNeil who got me hooked in the first place, Mr Large who got the surgery just right, Dr Kumud Dhital for his needlework and continual support and encouragement and Dr Peter Hopkins, who was true to his promise to get me through the first few months. Thanks, too, to Dr Sivasothy, Dr Parameshwar and Dr Parmar for all their hard work sorting out my medication and tolerance of my lists. To the nurses on the Critical Care Unit and Mallard Ward, the phlebotomists, physiotherapists, dieticians and pharmacists – in fact, the whole place is a model of what good medical care should be. Dr Richard Stevens and staff at East Oxford Health Centre have provided me with excellent medical treatment and support, and my thanks and apologies, also, to Dr Grant Lee for putting up with me through my stroppy childhood. In Oxford, I am grateful to Dr Brian Gribbin and Dr Adrian Banning for their medical care and encouragement.

My great thanks and love to my family and our friends who have done the whole thing with us. My father, John Sanders, who sadly died in January 2006, gave me so much love, help and encouragement.

My mother Barbara, my sisters, Annie Sanders and Chris Varney, and my brother, Rob, have been my family in the family sense of the word – always there, holding hands, nagging and cajoling and making us laugh. Jacqueline Tonin, Cath Dendy, Sue Ash, Elaine Fullard, Amanda Milligan, Anna Turner, Jonathan Holley, Ann Perry, Anthony Swift, Frank and Annie Wills, Jane and Roben Hera and all our neighbours, have been perfect friends in all sorts of ways – the party was for all of you and more.

This book was born out of a drunken conversation over a pizza during the British Association for Behavioural and Cognitive Psychotherapy conference in York in July 2003. Kevin Meares, Helen Jenkins, Damian Gardner and James Bennett-Levy encouraged me to write about my experiences, for better or worse and I thank Damian and Kevin for chasing me up and reading the manuscript. Thanks, also, to Anita Allinson for her comments and Rob Stepney for his photography and encouragement. I am enormously grateful to Brian Thompson for sweet-talking me to do a proper job of writing this book, then reading and rereading, cajoling and criticising me into finishing it. Also, to Elizabeth North for her encouragement and comments on my manuscript. My thanks to both of you for your interest. I am grateful to Dr Jas Parmar, Dr Mike Burch and Dr Annie Sanders for checking the medical content of the book: any errors are my full responsibility.

I am dedicating this book to three people. First, my mother Barbara, who has been my help and guide throughout my life. I've never felt alone in my struggles with my heart and she has taught me a great deal about acceptance and just getting on with whatever needs to be done as well as how to learn from whatever life throws at us. Secondly, to my love and husband Mo Chandler, the hero of this book, more special and more of a gift from the gods than he will ever realise. And thirdly, to my donor, who would by now be thirty-five, a young woman who died too soon but will never be forgotten. Thank you.

Resources

Books and publications

Finn, Robert (2000) *Organ Transplants. Making the Most of your Gift of Life*. Sebastopol, CA: O'Reilly.

Friedman, Rosemary (2001) *Intensive Care*. London: House of Stratus.

Hatton, Jo (1996) *Future Conditional: My Heart and Lung Transplant*. Castleford, Yorkshire: Yorkshire Arts Circus.

Living with Congenital Heart Disease. Information and Support for Teenagers and Adults. Published by the British Heart Foundation, available from www.bhf.org.uk

Tilney, Nicholas (2003) *Transplant. From Myth to Reality*. New York: Yale University Press.

Organisations and websites

UK Transplant
National organisation overseeing the allocation of donated organs, and providing information about organ donation and transplantation. Includes the organ donation register. www.uktransplant.org.uk

TIME: Transplants in Mind
A charity run to promote awareness of organ and tissue donation for transplantation. TIME actively promotes organ donation, co-ordinating volunteers and educational activities. www.transplantsinmind.co.uk

Transplant Support Network

A nationwide network that offers support to patients, families and carers of organ transplants, by contact with someone who has undergone the process. Helpline: 0800 027 4490/1; email: tsn@btconnect.com; www.transplantsupportnetwork.org.uk

John Fisher's website

John Fisher has set up a website based on his experience of a heart transplant in 2000, with information, message board and contact details. www.heart-transplant.co.uk

GUCH: Grown-Up Congenital Hearts

A charity, supported by the British Heart Foundation, to provide information and support for young people and adults who were born with a heart condition, and their families. Helpline: 0800 854 759; www.guch.org.uk

Dipex

Dipex was set up to give people a wide variety of personal experiences of health and illness, giving information on treatment choices and where to go for support. It has modules for parents of children with congenital heart disease, those facing heart failure and possible transplant, and will include further modules on other organ transplants. www.dipex.org

Julia Polak Research Trust

The Julia Polak Research Trust was set up to support medical research into ways of repairing or replacing damaged or diseased human organs and tissues, mainly in the field of tissue engineering and regenerative medicine. www.polak-transplant.med.ic.ac.uk

Transplant Sports Association of Great Britain

A charity organising sports and social events for transplant recipients, to show the benefits of transplantation and promote organ donation. http://tsuk.nemisys1.uk.com

To join the NHS Organ Donor Register:
Telephone 0845 60 60 400
www.uktransplant.org.uk